FIRST IMPRESSION 10,000 COPIES
SECOND IMPRESSION 10,000 COPIES
THIRD IMPRESSION 10,000 COPIES
FOURTH IMPRESSION 10,000 COPIES
FIFTH IMPRESSION 10,000 COPIES
SIXTH IMPRESSION 10,000 COPIES
SEVENTH IMPRESSION 10,000 COPIES
EIGHTH IMPRESSION 10,000 COPIES
NINTH IMPRESSION 10,000 COPIES
TENTH IMPRESSION 5,000 COPIES (owing to paper shortage)
ELEVENTH IMPRESSION 3,000 COPIES (owing to paper shortage)
TWELFTH IMPRESSION 3,000 COPIES (owing to paper shortage)
THIRTEENTH IMPRESSION 5,000 COPIES (owing to paper shortage)

THE TALES THE LETTERS TELL.

Book IV.

The Haunt of the Dragon Fly (page 89)

THE TALES THE LETTERS TELL.
Book IV.

TALES OF ROMANCE
AND REALITY.

Illustrated by
Robert Eadie, R.S.W.

LONDON AND GLASGOW:
The Grant Educational Co., Ltd.
1946

CONTENTS.

*The titles of poems are printed in italics.

CHRISTMAS DAY IN THE MINES

In a small cabin in an American mining town, away up amid the snow-clad, rock-bound peaks of the mountains, sat a woman, dressed in black, holding upon her knee a bright-eyed, sunny-faced little girl about five years old, while a little boy lay upon a bear-skin before the open fireplace. It was Christmas Eve, and the woman sat gazing into the fireplace. She was yet young, and, as the glowing flames lit up her face, its sadness could be easily seen.

Mary Stewart was the widow of Alec Stewart, and but two years before they had lived comfortably and happily, in a camp near the river. Alec was a brawny miner ; but the explosion of a blast in an underground tunnel had blotted out his life in an instant, leaving his family without a protector and in poverty. His daily wages had been their sole support. Now that he was gone, what could they do ?

With her little family Mrs. Stewart had moved to another camp, where she earned a scanty livelihood by washing clothes for the miners. Hers was a hard lot. But the brave little woman toiled on, cheered by the thought that her daily labours stood between her darling little ones and the gaunt wolf of starvation.

Jack Dawson, a strong, honest miner, was passing the cabin this Christmas Eve, when the voice of the little girl within attracted his attention. Jack possessed a great love for children, and, although his manly spirit would have abhorred the very thought of prying, he could not resist the temptation to steal up to the window for a moment to listen to the sweet, prattling voice. The first words he caught were :

" Before father died we always had Christmas, hadn't we, mother ? "

" Yes, Totty, darling ; but father earned money enough to afford to make his little pets happy at least once a year. You must remember, Totty, that we are very poor, and, although mother works very, very hard, she can scarcely earn enough to supply us with food and clothes."

Jack Dawson still lingered outside. He could not leave, although he felt ashamed of himself for listening.

" We hung up our stockings last Christmas, didn't we, mother ? " continued the little girl.

" Yes, Totty ; but we were poor then, and Santa

Claus never notices really poor people. He gave you a little candy then, just because you were such good children."

"Is we any poorer now, mother?"

"Oh, yes, much poorer. He would never notice us at all now."

Jack Dawson heard a tremor of sadness in the widow's voice as she uttered these last words, and he wiped a dampness from his eyes.

"Where's our clean stockings, mother? I'm going to hang mine up, anyhow; maybe he will come as he did before, just because we try to be good children," said Totty.

"It will be no use, my darling, I am sure he will not come," and tears gathered in the mother's eyes as she thought of her empty purse.

"I don't care; I'm going to try, anyhow. Please get one of my stockings, mother," said Totty.

Jack Dawson's generous heart swelled until it seemed to be bursting from his bosom. He heard the patter of little bare feet upon the cabin floor as Totty ran about hunting her and Benny's stockings, and, after she had hung them up, heard her sweet voice as she wondered over and over again if Santa Claus would really forget them. He heard the mother, in a choking voice, tell her treasures to get ready for bed; heard them lisp their childish prayers, the little girl concluding: "And please tell good Santa Claus that we are very poor, but that we love him as much as rich children do.—Amen."

After they were in bed, through a small rent in the plain white curtain he saw the widow sitting before the fire, her face buried in her hands, and weeping bitterly. On a peg, just over the fireplace, hung two little patched and faded stockings. At last he could stand it no longer, and moved softly away from the window to the rear of the cabin, where some objects fluttering in the wind caught his eye. Among these he searched until he found a little blue stocking, which he removed from the line, folded gently, and placed in his overcoat pocket. Then he set out for the main street of the camp, and entered Harry Hawk's gambling hall, the largest in the place, where a host of miners and gamblers were at play. Jack was well known in the camp, and, when he got on a chair and called for attention,

the hum of voices and clicking of ivory checks suddenly ceased. In an earnest voice he told what he had seen and heard, repeating every word of the conversation between the mother and her children. At the end he said :

" Boys, I think I know you, every one of you, an' I know just what kind o' metal yer made of. I 've an idee that Santy Claus knows jist whar that cabin's situated, an' I 've an idee he' ll find it afore mornin'. Hyar 's one of the little gal's stock'ns thet I hooked off'n the line. The daddy o' them little ones was a good, hard-workin' miner, an' he crossed the range in the line o' duty, jist as any one of us is liable to do in our dangerous business. Hyar goes a twenty-dollar piece right down in the toe, and hyar I lay the stockin' on this card table—now chip in, much or little, as ye kin afford."

Bronky Clark, a gambler, left the table, picked up the little stocking carefully, and looked at it tenderly ; and when he laid it down another twenty had gone into the toe to keep company with the one placed there by Dawson.

Another and another man came up, until the foot of the stocking was well filled, and then came a cry from the gaming tables, " Pass her round, Jack."

At the word he lifted it from the table and started round the hall. Before he had circulated it at half-a-dozen tables it showed signs of bursting beneath the weight of gold and silver coin, and a strong coin bag, such as is used for sending treasure by express,

was procured, and the stocking was placed in it.
The round of the hall was now made, but in the
meantime the story had spread all over the camp.
From the various saloons came messages saying :
"Send the stockin' round the camp: the boys
are a-waitin' for it." With a party at his heels,
Jack went from saloon to saloon. Games ceased
and tipplers left the bars as they entered each place,
and everybody crowded up to tender his Christmas
gift to the miner's widow and orphans. Anyone
who has lived in the far Western camps and is
acquainted with the generosity of Western men
will feel no surprise that, after the round had been
made, the little blue stocking and the heavy canvas
bag contained over eight thousand dollars in gold
and silver coin.

Horses were procured, and a party was dispatched
to the large town near, from which they returned
before daybreak with toys, clothing, and provisions
in endless variety. Arranging their gifts in proper
shape, and securely tying the mouth of the bag of
coin, the party noiselessly repaired to the widow's
humble cabin. The bag was first laid on the step,
and the other articles were piled in a heap over it.
On the top was laid the lid of a large pasteboard
box, on which was written with a piece of charcoal :

"Santy Claus doesn't allways giv poor folks the
cold shoulder in this camp."

Christmas Day dawned bright and beautiful.

Mrs. Stewart arose, and a shadow of pain crossed

her face as the empty little stockings caught her mother's eye. She cast a hurried glance toward the bed where her darlings lay sleeping, and murmured :

"O God! how dreadful is poverty!"

She built a glowing fire, and set about preparing their frugal breakfast. When it was almost ready she approached the bed, kissed the little ones until they were wide awake, and lifted them to the floor. With eager haste Totty ran to the stockings, only to turn away sobbing as though her heart would break. Tears blinded the mother, and, clasping her little girl to her heart she said in a choking voice :

"Never mind, my darling; next Christmas I am sure mother will be rich, and then Santa Claus will bring us lots of nice things."

"Oh, mother, mother!"

The exclamation came from little Benny, who had opened the door and was standing gazing in amazement upon the wealth of gifts there displayed.

Mrs. Stewart sprang to his side, and looked down in speechless astonishment. There were sacks of flour, hams, canned fruits, coffee, tea, and sugar, new dress goods, a handsome warm woollen shawl for the widow, shoes, stockings, hats, mittens and clothing for the children, a great wax doll that could open and shut its eyes for Totty, and a beautiful red sledge for Benny. All were carried inside amidst laughter and tears.

" Bring in the sack of salt, Totty, and that is all," said the mother. " Is not God good to us ? "

" I can't, mamma ; it 's frozen to the step."

The mother stooped and took hold of it, and lifted harder and harder till she raised it from the step. Her cheek blanched as she noted its great weight, and breathlessly she carried it in and laid it upon the breakfast table. With trembling fingers she loosened the string and emptied the contents upon the table—gold and silver, more than she had ever thought of in her wildest dreams of comfort, and almost buried in the pile lay Totty's little blue stocking.

Jack Dawson's burly form moved from behind a tree a short distance away, and sneaked off along the cutting, great crystal tears chasing each other down his face.

Exercises.

I.

1. Why was Mrs. Stewart so poor ?
2. How did she earn her living ?
3. How did Jack Dawson discover that the children would have no presents on Christmas Day ?
4. What did Mrs. Stewart say when Totty hoped that Santa Claus would bring presents to her ?
5. How did Jack Dawson collect money for the widow ?
6. For what did Mrs. Stewart mistake the bag of money ?

II.

1. Tell this story using the following headings :—

    (a) Jack Dawson hears Mrs. Stewart and her
        children talking.
    (b) He goes to a saloon and tells his friends
        what he has seen.
    (c) Money is collected to buy presents.
    (d) A party go to purchase the presents.
    (e) The widow finds the presents.
2. A few months after the event Jack Dawson fell
   ill. Invent a story to show how Mrs. Stewart,
   without knowing who had helped her, repaid him.
3. Make a little play out of Christmas Day in the
   Mines.

The Green Lady.

A lovely Green Lady
Embroiders and stitches
Sweet flowers in the meadows,
On banks and in ditches.

All day she is sewing—
Embroidering all night—
For she works in the darkness
As well as the light.

She makes no mistake in
The silks which she uses,
And all her gay colours
She carefully chooses.

The Green Lady.

She fills nooks and corners
With blossoms so small,
Where none but the fairies
Will see them at all.

She sews them so quickly,
She trims them so neatly,
Though much of her broidery
Is hidden completely.

She scatters her tapestry,
Scented and sweet,
In the loneliest places
Or 'neath careless feet ;

For bee, or for bird folk,
For children like me,
But the lovely Green Lady
No mortal may see.

C. D. Cole.

The Cock and the Fox

Persons:

Chanticleer, the Cock ; *Pertelot*, the Hen ;
Reynard, the Fox.

Scene—A Cottage Garden.

Pertelot.—My dear Chanticleer, last night as you stood on your perch I heard you groaning in your sleep, as if you were afraid of something. Dear heart, what was the matter ?

Chanticleer.—Madam, I dreamt that I was in terrible danger. Even now I feel afraid when I think of it.

Pertelot.—What did you dream ?

Chanticleer.—I dreamt that, as I strutted up and down, I saw a creature like a dog, which tried to seize me, and to kill me. His colour was a tawny red. His ears and tail were tipped with black. He

had a long, narrow nose, and two glittering eyes.
Doubtless it was this dream which caused me to
moan in my sleep.

Pertelot.—Fie upon you, you coward. I am
ashamed to have a coward for my husband. How

dare you tell me that you are afraid of anything,
and particularly of a silly, empty dream, which
came to you, probably, because you ate too much
supper last night? Wise men bid us pay no heed
to dreams.

Take some medicine. There is no chemist here
to whom you can go, but I will advise you what green
herbs you may find in the garden which will cure
you, so that you shall dream no more such dreams.
Husband, cheer up : to be afraid because of a dream
is foolish indeed.

Chanticleer.—I am much obliged to you for your advice, Pertelot. Nevertheless, I am not convinced. In old books, written by learned men, I have read many instances of dreams which have come true. They tell us that dreams are signs showing what will happen to us, or that they have a hidden meaning.

One such story I remember particularly well. It was about two men who were travelling together. One of them slept at an inn one night, while his fellow, because there was no room in the inn, had to sleep elsewhere. The first traveller dreamt that his companion had been killed during the night, and when he awoke in the morning, he found that it was so in very truth. And, in consequence of this dream, he was able to discover those who had done the wicked deed, and they were punished as they deserved.

Remember, too, how Pharaoh dreamt that seven fat and well-favoured kine came up out of the Nile and that they were followed by seven lean kine which devoured them. Joseph explained this dream, and showed that it meant that there would be seven years of plenty in the land of Egypt, and after them seven years of famine. All happened exactly as he foretold, which proves that dreams are not idle fancies, but are worthy of attention. Therefore, Pertelot, nobody should be heedless of dreams. Did not Pharaoh's butler and baker dream of things which actually came to pass?

Pertelot.—Fie upon you, you faint-hearted coward!

Chanticleer.—No, no, I am not a coward. But I ought to heed my dream. Did not Andromache, Hector's wife, the night before he was slain, dream that if her husband went into the battle on the next day he would be slain? He laughed at her fears, and went out to fight. And that day he was slain by Achilles. Did not Cæsar's wife dream that he would be killed?

And so I feel sure that this vision of the night warns me of some misfortune that will befall me. I hate medicine. I do not believe that medicine will do me any good. Medicine tastes like poison, and I will have none of it.

But now, let us stop this. I am no coward, and I will show no fear. Let us be happy while we can.

[*The cock and hen cluck loudly, and walk up and down, pecking at the corn which lies on the ground around them. While they do so, a fox, unseen by them, creeps into the cabbages, and fixes his eyes upon Chanticleer.*]

Chanticleer.—Cock-a-doodle-do!

Pertelot.—Cluck-cluck!

Chanticleer.—My dear Pertelot, the sun is high. Listen to the singing of the birds! Do you see how beautiful the fresh flowers are? Look, there is a butterfly, which has lighted on the cabbages. I will catch it, and eat it.

[The cock catches sight of the fox lying hidden among the cabbages.]

Chanticleer (in terror).—Cock-cock!

Reynard.—Noble Sir, what is the matter? Do not be afraid. What cause have I to harm you? I have only come to hear you crow. You have a beautiful voice : you can sing like an angel. I never knew anyone who could sing so well, except my lord your father, upon whose soul be peace. Both he and your mother condescended to visit my humble dwelling in the hills, and right glad I was to conduct them there. My wife and children welcomed them heartily.

I will say, I never heard anyone—except your father—singing in the morning, when the sun rises, as you can do. Your father sang with all his might. He would hold his head up, and stretch his long, thin neck, and shut his eyes, and crow with all his heart. And he was as wise as his voice was tuneful. Will you not crow for me?

Chanticleer.—Gentle fox, I should be ashamed not to grant so modest a request, although I cannot hope to equal my father. Cock-a-doodle———

[As he begins to crow, after beating his wings, the fox leaps out of the covert, seizes him by the neck and rushes away towards the woods. All the hens begin to make a noise, and fly up and down, so that they attract the notice of the people in the cottage, who run out and chase the fox.]

B

Chanticleer (to himself).—Wretched bird that I am!
He has got me now, because of my pride, and because I listened to his flattery, and he will eat me.
But I will see whether I cannot play upon him the
same trick, and perhaps I shall be able to escape.

(Aloud)—Sir Fox, if I were you, I would say to
all these people : " You can't catch me. You may
as well go back. I have got Chanticleer. He is
mine, and I will devour him, in spite of you all."

Reynard.—Yes, I will! [*as he opens his mouth to
utter these words the cock struggles free, and flies
up into a tree.*]

Alas! Chanticleer, I am afraid you feel insulted.
But, please do not suppose that I was going to hurt
you. I had no such evil intention. Come down,
do, and I will tell you what I meant to do.

Chanticleer.—No, no, a man who is deceived twice
is a fool indeed. I am safe where I am, and here
I shall remain till you are gone. You will not get
me to crow again by your flattery.

Reynard.—Now I see, both by your behaviour
and by mine, that silence is best, and that he is above
all others unwise who talks and chatters when he
should hold his peace.

Adapted from Chaucer's " Canterbury Tales."

Exercises.
I.
1. Why was Pertelot angry with Chanticleer?
2. What did Chanticleer think to be the cause of his
   dream? What did Pertelot think was the cause?

3. Why did Reynard persuade the cock to crow?
4. How did the cock escape from the fox?
5. What did the fox say when Chanticleer had escaped, and refused to come down from the tree?

II.

Find another word which has the same meaning as each of the following :—danger, glittering, beautiful, humble, heartily, devour, evil, unwise.

III.

1. Make a little play out of either of the following tales, putting in the proper stage directions :—
   Cinderella.   The Story of Joseph.
2. Tell the story of the Cock and the Fox in your own words.

Poetry.

In this book, among the other pieces, there are a number of poems. People sometimes wonder what is the difference between poetry and ordinary writing, which is called prose, and not seldom they conclude that there is something mysterious about poetry, and so they fail to understand it. This is a great pity, for poetry is not a mysterious thing, and anyone who has not learnt, before growing into a man or a woman, what poetry is, anyone who has not learnt to love poetry, has missed a means of obtaining great and pure pleasure.

The simplest thing that could be said about poetry is that a poem consists of words. Every craftsman works with some material : the builder uses brick, stone, and wood ; the potter uses clay ; the poet employs words. He does this skilfully, and tries, with his words, to make something beautiful. A poem consists of words skilfully and beautifully arranged.

Now the beauty of words lies in their sound. Whatever else it may be, and above all else, a poem is a piece of music. Poetry is music. The poem called " The Barrel Organ," which is printed on page 51, shows this very well. In each line of this poem there are eight beats :—

Go dówn to Kéw in lílac-tíme, in lílac-tíme, in lílac-
         tíme.

      *   *   *   *   *   *   *   *   *

And yóu shall wánder hánd in hánd with lóve in
         súmmer's wónderland . . .

Secondly, in many poems the lines, taking them in pairs, end in words that are similar, but not exactly alike, in their sound. Thus the first poem in this book contains *good. could; top, hop; taller, smaller.* Such similar endings we call rhymes. The music of poetry comes mainly from the way in which the beats are arranged, and from the endings. The first is called the rhythm, the second are rhymes. How dull sounds this description of sunset :—

> The western waves of ebbing day
> Rolled o'er the glen their level path ;
> But not a setting beam could shine
> Within the dark ravines below.

compared with :—

> The western waves of ebbing day
> Rolled o'er the glen their level way ;
> But not a setting beam could glow
> Within the dark ravines below,

and all the music is taken away, and the beauty of the lines is destroyed, if the piece is altered to

O'er the glen the western waves of ebbing day rolled their level path, but within the dark ravines underneath not a setting beam could shine.

There are many different kinds of rhythm : if the pieces of poetry in this book are read through one after another, it will be seen that their rhythms are not all alike. In each line of " The Barrel Organ " there are eight beats. In " Lochinvar " (p. 85) there are only four beats in each line. At the end of each line is a slight pause.

Some poems are divided into verses or stanzas, and there are many different kinds of these. Other poems run straight on without a break.

Rhythm and rhyme are the two principal ways in which poems are made musical, but there are others that, although they are less important, are very charming. No one can fail to observe what a tune sings in

> Ye mariners of England
> That guard our native seas,
> Whose flag has braved a thousand years
> The battle and the breeze.

Many poems, besides being music, contain pictures. Some poems are simply clear descriptions of things, which means that they are pictures in words. Others are partly made up of such pictures.

The poem called "The Windmill," on page 63, is a picture in which all the details are drawn as faithfully as if they were sketched with a pencil or painted with a brush. The first verse brings before us the general scenery, the corn fields and the meadows. Next we see the miller standing by, reckoning and writing down the number of sacks of flour, and we see the great vans of the mill circling round. We behold, too, the white dust that covers everything.

More than this, a poet can make us imagine that we hear sounds, as well as seeing objects. In the same poem, "The Windmill," the creaking of the sails, and the shuddering noise of the timbers of which the mill is built are both to be heard, so that we gain a completer idea of the mill than a mere picture could give us. In this way a poet has some advantage over a painter.

When anyone is able to make a reader see in his fancy what is being described in words, he can tell a story in a very interesting way. A story may be dull or interesting. If it is vivid it is more likely to claim our attention than if the facts are related in a matter-of-fact manner. Therefore a poet, if he chooses, can tell a tale. Many poets have chosen to write poems which recount an incident, or which tell a long story. "Lochinvar" is one of these.

The story is :—Lochinvar rode speedily on a swift horse to Netherby Hall, hoping to arrive before the maiden whom he wished to marry was wedded to another. But he was too late, and he reached the Hall to find that the wedding was about to begin, and that the guests were already assembled. Though a dance was in progress, he dismounted and entered the hall, and asked for the favour of one dance with the bride. He drank her health, and then they danced. When they were opposite the door he suddenly lifted her on his horse, sprang up before her, and galloped away. As soon as those who stood by had recovered from their surprise, they saddled their horses and started in pursuit, but they did not succeed in over-taking him.

The poet has adorned this little story with music and with pictures, in the way that has already been described, and by so doing has made it far more beautiful than it could ever have been if told in the ordinary way.

Even yet, however, we have not found out all the objects that poets have in view when they write poems. In fact, to give a complete account would be impossible, because the different kinds of poems, their various beauties, and the purposes of their writers, are very numerous. They are really numberless.

Some poems are sad, some are comical and gay : some paint pictures, others tell stories ; there are songs and hymns, battle poems, poems about plants and animals, ballads, and many others.

One thing more we must notice, if we are to understand what a poem is. A poet often desires to tell us how he feels. There is a poem by a famous poet called Wordsworth which begins :

> My heart leaps up when I behold
> A rainbow in the sky.

Another by a poet named Browning commences :

> Oh, to be in England
> Now that April 's there !

The first of these expresses the poet's feeling at the sight of the rainbow : the second expresses a wish. The poem beginning " If I were Lord of Tartary " (page 36) is a kind of day-dream in which the author lets his fancy roam at sweet will, and in which he tells us what he would like to do if he had the power.

The most wonderful glory of poetry is that it can do all these at the same time. While telling us a story in a musical manner, and painting for us, often by a little touch, a lovely picture, a poet can communicate to us the most secret feelings of his heart. And he does this in the noblest manner, and makes us free of his inmost soul. That is why poetry is a gift which we should admire, cherish, and use.

Exercises.

1. What is it that makes words beautiful?
2. From the poems in this book pick out a verse which seems to you beautiful, and say why you consider it to be so.
3. Find a word which rhymes with each of the following words: beam, night, sky, gold, stone, home, blue, three, sleep, bird.
4. Are there any humorous poems in this book? If so, name them.
5. Which poems in this book tell a story?
6. Find in the poems contained in this book a verse which is a picture in words.
7. Complete the following verses by putting suitable words where there is a word missing.

(a) I like the hunting of the hare
    Better than that of the fox;
  I like the joyous morning air,
    And the crowing of the ——.

(b) The moon is up: the stars are bright,
    The wind is fresh and ——,
  We're out to seek for gold to-night
    Across the silver sea.

(c) The pebbles, they were smooth and round
    And warm upon my hands,
  Like little people I had found
    Sitting among the ——.

(d) The western wave was all aflame,
    The day was well-nigh done!
  Almost upon the western wave
    Rested the broad bright ——.

The Wind and the Peasant

Long ago there lived a poor peasant named Peter Hodge who had very little beyond a wife and a large family of children whose appetites he found very difficult to satisfy. One day he went out into his little field to cut and thresh his wheat; but, after he had finished, the wind blew boisterously and swept away every grain of his corn. Enraged at this cruel theft, the poor man cried, "I'll seek the Wind till I find him, and I'll tell him what labour I gave to growing my corn, which he has wasted and destroyed." Straightway he took leave of his wife, and went out in search of the Wind.

He travelled until he came to the edge of a great forest, and on the borders of that forest he saw a hut. The door of the hovel was open, and through the doorway the peasant saw an old man of gigantic stature stretched upon the floor asleep. It was no other than the Wind himself. "Good morning," cried the peasant. "Good health to you," said the giant, awaking ; "What are you seeking?" "I am wandering through the world to find the Wind," said Peter, "and when I find him I shall upbraid him because of the wrong he has done me." "What wrong has he done you?" asked the giant, sitting up.

"While I was reaping my little field of corn," replied Peter, "the Wind came and scattered every bit of it in an instant, so that there was not a single particle of it left. It was all I had, and in the sweat of my brow did I sow and reap and thresh it." "My son," said the giant, "I am the Wind. I am very sorry. I did not know that I had harmed you." "Give me back my corn," cried Peter. "No," answered the Wind, "I cannot do that. Yet something I can do. I will give you an enchanted sack. Whenever you want a meal, say 'Food and drink!' and immediately you shall have what you desire. So now you will possess the wherewithal to feed your wife and children."

Peter Hodge was full of gratitude, and thanked the Wind for his courtesy. "Go home," said the Wind, "and be sure to enter no tavern to drink by the way." "Very well," said the peasant : "I will not," and he bade farewell to the Wind and departed.

He had not proceeded far before he passed by an inn, and at once felt a burning thirst consuming him. Forgetting his promise, he entered, sat down, and called for drink. But in a moment his curiosity and desire to test the powers of the magic sack over-

came him, and he said, " Food and drink!" to the
sack, and immediately the table in front of him was
covered with all manner of good things. When
the inn keeper saw what had happened he was
amazed, and coveted the sack, and determined to
steal it.

So he offered drink to Hodge, who was so simple
that he did not perceive the inn-keeper's subtle
malice and cunning, and drank till he became in-
toxicated and fell asleep. While he was snoring
with his head on the table, the inn-keeper changed
the sack for another.

Next morning the peasant awoke early, and, taking
up the substituted sack, departed homewards.

When he came to his cottage he cried, " Open
the door, wife; sit down at table; now we have
enough and to spare." The wife thought her husband had lost his senses, but, nevertheless, she and
her husband sat down. Then Peter exclaimed, " Food
and drink!" But the sack was silent and still.
Then the foolish peasant fell into a violent rage,
and set out to seek the Wind again, while his wife
began to rail, and to scold her husband.

He went again to the Wind, who said, when he
saw him, " Wherefore do you come hither, my friend?
Didn't I give you my magic sack?" "Your sack,"
answered Peter, " has been the cause of much harm
to me. You promised that it should give me food
and drink, but it will not do so. Give me something
else instead of it. Here it is."

The Wind looked at the sack which the country-man held out. "That is not my sack," he shouted. "You have been into an inn, although I told you to avoid taverns and strong drink. However, though it is your own fault that you have lost the sack, I will give you a goat. Whenever you want any money, say to it, 'Money I lack!' and it will scatter gold and silver coins for you on the floor. Only, remem-ber this: go not into a tavern. For, if you do, I shall know; and, if you come to me a third time, you will have cause to remember it."

"Very well," said Peter, "I'll not enter any tavern," and he took the goat, and went away.

But when Peter Hodge came to the same tavern where he had been robbed of his sack, a strong desire to enter it again seized him, and he did so. As soon as the inn-keeper saw him leading his goat into the tavern, he called out, "Leave your goat outside." "No," said the simple peasant, "I dare not do that: for this is a marvellous goat, which can scatter money whenever I command it to do so." And to testify to the truth of his words, he made the goat scatter money for him, picked it all up, and put it into his pockets.

The inn-keeper, who was very greedy, opened his eyes with amazement when he saw this, and determined to steal the goat as he had stolen the sack. Accordingly, he set food and ale before the foolish countryman, and with deceit in his heart warned him not to drink too much.

The peasant marvelled at his seeming straight-forwardness, and, forgetting all else, drank many tankards of ale, till his wits wandered and left him, and he fell asleep. And, while he was sleeping off the effects of his carousal, the inn-keeper replaced his goat by another which resembled it very closely.

On awaking, Peter started out with no more suspicion than on the previous occasion, and soon arrived at his home. Before he had reached the door, he cried, "Now we shall have everything we want, for I am rich." "What have you brought back?" asked his wife. "I have brought this goat," replied he. "Is that all?" said the good woman. "What good can we get from a wretched goat? Where shall we find the money to buy food for it?" "Ah," her husband said, "I will show you. Spread a cloth on the floor, and you shall see what you shall see."

The poor wife thought that her husband was surely mad. Still, she did as he requested. Then he pulled the goat on the cloth and exclaimed, "Money I lack! money I lack! money I lack!" But the creature, as was natural, stood still, stared at him stupidly, and did nothing else.

Peter Hodge was now very much offended, and said, "I'll go back to the Wind again, and tell him what a fool he has made me appear to my wife." And his wife put everything straight, and reproached her husband.

Then the peasant came to the Wind for the third

time. As soon as the Wind saw him, he roared, "Oh, you have come back again, have you? Surely there is no turning a fool from his folly. This time I'll give you my drum, and that is something that will teach you to remember my warnings."

With that the Wind said to a little drum that lay in a corner of the hut, "Out of the drum, my merry men!" and immediately six broad-shouldered,

strong-armed dwarfs, with sticks in their hands, leaped out of the drum, set upon Peter, and gave him a sound thrashing.

"Oh! oh!" he cried. "Forgive me! Be merciful! I'll not come again, and I'll do all your behests."

"Into the drum, my merry men!" said the Wind. "Now," said he, when the dwarfs had disappeared, while Peter rubbed himself and stood trembling with fear, "I'll give you the drum. Go to that tavern. If you have learnt your lesson, you will not drink. And if you have any wits, you will know what to do."

Peter had not much sense, but he had enough to comprehend that he could recover his sack and his goat. With many thanks to the Wind he picked up the drum and departed. When he reached the tavern, the inn-keeper recognised him, and said, "It's no use your coming here, for I have no more drink to serve you with."

"I want no drink from you," replied Peter in a surly tone: "I want my sack and my goat." "Your sack and your goat!" screamed the rascal. "What are you talking about? Get out of this house, or it will be the worse for you."

"Out of the drum, my merry men!" said the peasant. Immediately the six dwarfs rushed from the drum, and, falling on the inn-keeper, began to belabour him fiercely. "Oh! oh! spare my life," wailed the inn-keeper in a moment. "Spare my life, and I will give you everything I have." Then Peter called off his terrible servants, and the inn-keeper quickly restored to him the sack and the goat; for he was more dead than alive.

When the peasant reached home, he took in with him his drum, his sack, and his goat. Spreading a cloth on the floor, he cried, "Money I lack!" and immediately the goat scattered gold and silver on the cloth, while Peter's wife and children stood round.

"Now we will have something to eat," he said, and, sitting down at the table, he uttered the words "Food and drink!" whereupon a rich repast was laid before the astonished family.

While all were dining, Peter told them everything that had happened, and how he had lost and regained the magic sack and the enchanted goat. At the end he said : "The last present which the wind gave to me was this drum. This will defend us when we need defence ; and, since I have learnt to be a fool no more, I warn you that it will be very painful for anyone who reproaches me or thinks me mad." His wife understood exactly what he meant, and she paid attention to his words, so that to this day she and her children have not seen what lurks within that drum.

Exercises.

I.

1. Why did the peasant seek the Wind ?
2. What presents did the Wind give to Peter ?
3. How did he lose the first two presents he received ?
4. How did he recover them ?
5. What kind of creature is the Wind, in this story ?
6. How did Peter Hodge secure the respect and obedience of his wife and children ?

II.

1. Tell the story of King Alfred and the cakes.
2. Relate this story as the innkeeper would tell it.
3. Describe a mill driven by a water-wheel (page 63).

If I were Lord of Tartary.

(From "Songs of Childhood," published by Messrs. Longmans, Green & Co., by
special permission of the Author and Publishers.)

If I were Lord of Tartary,
Myself and me alone,
My bed should be of ivory,
Of beaten gold my throne ;
And in my court would peacocks flaunt
And in my forests tigers haunt,
And in my pools great fishes slant
Their fins athwart the sun.

If I were Lord of Tartary,
Trumpeters every day
To every meal would summon me,
And in my courtyard bray ;
And in the evening lamps should shine,
Yellow as honey, red as wine,
While harp, and flute, and mandoline,
Made music sweet and gay.

If I were Lord of Tartary,
I'd wear a robe of beads,
White, and gold, and green they'd be,
And clustered thick as seeds ;
And ere should wane the morning-star
I'd don my robe and scimitar,
And zebras seven should draw my car
Through Tartary's dark glades.

"And in the evening lamps should shine" (page 36)

Lord of the fruits of Tartary,
Her rivers silver-pale !
Lord of the hills of Tartary,
Glen, thicket, wood and dale !
Her flashing stars, her scented breeze,
Her trembling lakes, like foamless seas,
Her bird-delighting citron-trees
In every purple vale.

Walter de la Mare.

The Merchant of Venice.

Centuries ago there lived in the famous city of Venice two friends, whose names were Antonio and Bassanio. Antonio was a merchant who traded with foreign countries, with England, and Africa, and the East. Bassanio was not as rich as Antonio, and, indeed, at the time of which we write, he had very little money. Therefore, as he wished to marry a noble lady of Belmont, whose name was Portia, he asked his friend Antonio to lend him three thousand golden ducats.

Now Antonio had invested all his money in ships which were abroad on the high seas, so that he was not able to help Bassanio as he would have desired. The only way in which he could obtain such a large sum of money was to borrow it from a Jewish money-lender, whose name was Shylock. To Shylock accordingly he went.

Antonio had always treated Shylock with great contempt because he was not a Christian, and, in consequence, the Jew had conceived a great hatred for him. As soon as he heard that the merchant wished to borrow money from him, he saw an opportunity of harming Antonio and of thus satisfying his feeling of dislike. He said, " Signor Antonio, you have called me a dog and have spat upon my cloak when you have met me. Do you now come to borrow money from me? Can a dog lend you three thousand ducats? Nevertheless, to show you that I bear no grudge against you in my heart, I will lend you the money; nay, I will do more than that: I will lend it to you without taking proper security. I am sure that your ships will come home soon, and that you will be able to pay. Therefore, just for form's sake, instead of asking you to pledge to me something of value, let us agree, and have a written bond to that effect, that you shall allow me to cut off from your body, at whatsoever part I please, a pound of flesh, if my loan to you is not repaid within three months. This would only be in jest, of course." Shylock spoke thus from the cunning of his heart, and because of the bitter hatred he cherished against Antonio.

When he heard the terms which the Jew proposed, Bassanio felt misgivings, and did not wish Antonio to accept them. He said that he would prefer to go without the money rather than that Antonio should risk his life by placing it in this way in Shylock's

power. But Antonio laughed at his fears, made
the agreement, and handed the money to Bassanio.

A few days later Bassanio departed for Belmont
to ask Portia to marry him.

When Portia's father died he left a will in which
he directed that his daughter was to choose a husband
in a very peculiar manner. She was to have three
caskets made—one of gold, one of silver, and one
of lead—and in the last she was to place her portrait.
Every suitor who sought her hand was to be required
to choose the casket which contained the portrait.
If he chose aright, Portia had to marry him. On
the other hand, before choosing, he was to swear
that, if he was not successful in deciding which casket
held the picture, he would depart at once and would
never marry any woman. If Portia disobeyed the
instruction of the will, she was to lose all her property.

The fame of these strange conditions and of Portia's
wealth and beauty spread far and wide, so that men
came from all parts of the world to seek her in
marriage. Up to the present none had been so
fortunate as to decide upon the leaden casket.

As soon as Bassanio, who was accompanied by
a friend of his named Gratiano, arrived at Portia's
house, she was so impressed by his handsome form
and manly grace that she fell in love with him. Her
maid, Nerissa, was equally pleased with Gratiano.
The trial of the caskets was deferred for a few weeks,
in order that they might enjoy one another's company,
and during this time Gratiano and Nerissa agreed

that, if Bassanio should choose the right casket, they also would be married, so that a double wedding depended upon his success or failure.

When the appointed day came, Portia was very agitated and anxious. But Bassanio, who was as wise as he was handsome and courtly, opened the leaden casket and found therein the portrait, which showed him that Portia was to become his wife.

There was great rejoicing when this occurred, especially when Gratiano and Nerissa came forward and revealed their secret to Bassanio and Portia. Each lady gave her lover a ring, which he promised he would never part with, and each of them said that if he did give it to anyone, it would be a sign that he had ceased to be faithful and true.

Meanwhile, many important events had been taking place in Venice. Misfortune had overtaken both Shylock and Antonio. Shylock had a daughter named Jessica, who had learned to loathe her father's harsh and cruel disposition. She had fallen in love with a Venetian named Lorenzo, who persuaded her to run away with him to Genoa, taking with her as much of her father's money, and as many of his jewels, as she could find.

When Shylock discovered his losses, his rage and despair exceeded all bounds. At one moment he was overwhelmed with grief at the disappearance of Jessica, at the next the thought of his wealth being squandered at Genoa overcame him. He went about crying continually " Oh, my daughter! Oh, my ducats !" till his lamentations made him ridiculous, and the very boys in the streets began to follow him about, teasing him and shouting after him : "Oh, my daughter! Oh, my ducats !" This made him all the more eager to have his revenge upon Antonio.

Before long he had the opportunity, for Antonio's ships were all lost at sea. As soon as the day came, seeing that Antonio was not able to pay the debt, Shylock had him arrested, and went to the Duke to obtain leave to cut from Antonio's body, next to his heart, the pound of flesh which, he urged, was his by right of the Venetian law. In great misery Antonio wrote a letter to Bassanio, acquainting him with the facts, and urging him to return at once to Venice to bid farewell to his unfortunate friend, who was about to die a painful death at the hands of the Jew.

This letter reached Belmont just after Portia had become betrothed to Bassanio, and the news which it contained changed all their happiness into sorrow, as may be well imagined. They would have thought that Shylock would not be so heartless as to kill Antonio, but that Lorenzo and Jessica, who had left Genoa, happened to arrive at Belmont about the same time. Jessica assured them that her father would be pitiless, so great was his hatred of Antonio.

Therefore Portia urged Bassanio first to marry her, and then to hasten with all speed to Venice, also bidding him offer to Shylock the value of his debt six times over if he would release Antonio.

No sooner had Bassanio and Gratiano departed than Portia proceeded to put into execution a plan which she had formed to help Antonio. She committed the care of her house into the hands of Lorenzo and Jessica, telling them that she and Nerissa wished to retire to a monastery till their husbands' return. Then she said in private to Nerissa, " Come, Nerissa : we will see our husbands before they expect it : and we will see them in such a disguise that they shall not know us. Let us go dressed in men's clothes, I as a doctor of law, and you as his clerk." Nerissa being quite willing to obey her wishes, they started without delay.

They reached Venice on the very day that Shylock hoped to cut the forfeit from Antonio's heart. The Jew took his prisoner to the Duke's court, and sought for permission to execute his wicked will.

The Duke tried to move him from his purpose. He pointed out that Bassanio had offered him eighteen thousand ducats for his three thousand, that it was mere accident that had prevented Antonio from paying before the appointed day, that Antonio's flesh was worth nothing, and, finally, that Shylock ought to have mercy. But Shylock replied that he hated Antonio, and that that was sufficient reason for killing him. He said, too, that he took his stand upon the laws of the city ; and that if he was not allowed to have his bond, there was no force nor justice in these laws. The Duke hesitated, and then replied that he would not pronounce judgment until he had consulted Bellario, a learned lawyer of Padua, about the matter.

While he was speaking thus, Portia and Nerissa entered, bringing a letter from Bellario, whom they had visited during their journey, to ask for his advice.

The Duke read the letter, which informed him that Bellario himself, being sick, could not come, but that he had sent in his stead a young lawyer in whom he reposed great trust. Portia then asked Shylock to be merciful. But the inexorable Jew persisted in claiming his due. Portia told the Court that the Jew had the right to a pound of Antonio's flesh, according to the written bond which the un-happy merchant had given him.

When he heard this, Shylock was very pleased, and praised her. Once again she asked him to be merciful, to take thrice his money, and to surrender the bond. But he said, "I will not surrender it till I have the forfeit named in it. Let us proceed to judg-ment. There is no power on earth that can alter me. I want what is named in the bond, and nothing else."

At the sound of these dreadful words, Antonio bared his breast, and then Shylock took up his knife. But Portia said, " Wait a moment. You shall have what is named in the bond, and nothing else. The bond promises you a pound of flesh. Take it, then ; but, if you cut more than a pound, or less than a pound, or if you shed a drop of blood, you are guilty of murder, if Antonio dies, and all your possessions will be con-fiscated."

Shylock was thunderstruck at what Portia said, and, quickly changing his mind, offered to take the money which Bassanio had in court for him. But Portia interfered, and insisted that, as the Jew had already refused the ducats, he should have nothing but the exact penalty named in the bond. Moreover, she drew the Court's attention to another law, which laid down that, if anyone plotted against the life of a Venetian citizen, he should be punished with death, and that his goods should go, half to the State, and half to the person against whom he had plotted.

The tables were now turned. But the Duke spared Shylock's life, and Antonio resigned his right to half of Shylock's goods in favour of Lorenzo, his daughter's husband, on condition that the Jew became a Christian.

When Shylock had left the court, and Bassanio wished to pay the lawyer's fee, Portia would take nothing except the ring upon his finger. This was the ring which Bassanio had promised he would never give up to anyone. But it was impossible for him to refuse a request to the wise counsellor who had just saved Antonio's life, and he was obliged to part with the ring. In the same way Nerissa obtained her own ring from Gratiano.

Without any delay Portia and Nerissa hastened to Belmont, whither they were followed, a day later, by Bassanio, Antonio, and Gratiano. As soon as Nerissa saw her husband, she asked him where was the ring that she had given him as a pledge of

love, and she refused to believe that he had given
it to a lawyer's clerk as a fee. Portia heard the
two talking, and, joining in, expressed her disapproval
of Gratiano's action. Then Bassanio had to confess
that he also had given his ring away. Portia at first
pretended to be very angry, but after much banter-
ing she let Bassanio know that she herself was the
learned doctor of law who had rescued Antonio from
the clutches of the Jew.

And so all ended happily for everyone except Shylock, who was justly punished for his wickedness.

Exercises.
I.

1. For what purpose did Bassanio need money?
2. Why could not Antonio lend any money to Bassanio?
3. Give the reasons which Shylock had for hating
   Antonio.
4. What was the agreement made between Antonio
   and Shylock?
5. How did Bassanio succeed in gaining Portia in
   marriage?
6. Who was Jessica? How did she come to visit
   Belmont?
7. Why was Antonio unable to pay Shylock on the
   day fixed?
8. What was the plan which Portia formed to help
   Antonio?
9. How did Portia prevent Shylock from harming
   Antonio?
10. What was the fee which Portia demanded for
    her services as a lawyer?

11. How would Portia and Nerissa be able to prove to their husbands that they had been to Venice disguised as a lawyer and his clerk?

II.

1. What words have the opposite meaning of :— Famous, rich, friend, borrow, hatred, agree, bitter, accept, strange, handsome, begin, learned?

2. What is the meaning of :— Depart, despair, squander, imagine, accident, pronounce, sufficient, forfeit, thunderstruck, pretend, justly?

III.

1. Tell the Story of *The Merchant of Venice,* using the following headings :—

   (a) Antonio borrows money for Bassanio from Shylock.

   (b) Bassanio goes to Belmont and wins Portia.

   (c) Antonio is put in prison by Shylock.

   (d) Shylock goes to the Duke's court with Antonio.

   (e) Portia and Nerissa go to the Court and rescue Antonio.

   (f) Portia and Bassanio meet again at Belmont.

2. Write a letter from Nerissa to a friend telling the adventures which she had while she was disguised as a lawyer's clerk.

R. EADIE

Three of Æsop's Fables.

I.—MERCURY AND THE WOODMAN.

A woodman, while felling a tree which grew beside a river, let his axe drop by accident into a deep pool. Being thus deprived of the means of his livelihood, he sat down on the bank and began to lament his hard fate.   While he was so occupied, the god Mercury appeared before him, and asked him the cause of his despair.   As soon as he heard the story of the misfortune, Mercury plunged into the water, and, bringing up a golden axe, inquired if that was the axe that the woodman had lost. On hearing that it was not, he disappeared beneath the water a second time, returned with a silver axe in his hand, and again asked if that was the right axe. The woodman replied once more that it was not, where-upon Mercury dived into the pool for the third time, and this time brought up the axe that had fallen into the river. On the woodman claiming it joyfully, Mercury, pleased with his honesty, gave him the golden and silver axes in addition to his own.

The story of what had happened was related to his companions by the woodman when he returned home in the evening. One of them resolved to try whether he could not also secure the same good fortune. Accordingly he rose early next morning, ran to the river, and, throwing his axe into the pool, sat down on the bank to weep. Just as he had hoped, Mercury appeared, and, having learnt the cause of his grief, plunged into the stream and brought up a golden axe. Unable to resist the temptation, the workman seized it greedily, declaring that it was in very truth the axe that he had lost. Dis-pleased at his knavery, Mercury not only took away the golden axe, but refused to recover for him the axe which he had thrown into the pool.

II.—THE HARE AND THE TORTOISE.

A Hare one day ridiculed the short feet and the

slow pace of the Tortoise. The latter, laughing, said, "Though you be as swift as the wind, I will beat you in a race." The Hare, deeming this to be impossible, assented to the proposal, and fixed the prize to be awarded to the winner. On the day appointed for the race, they started together. The Tortoise never for a moment stopped, but went on with a slow, steady pace straight towards the end of the course. The Hare, trusting to his fleetness of foot, cared little about the race, and, lying down by the wayside, fell fast asleep. At last, waking up, and running as fast as he could, he saw the Tortoise about to reach the goal. He galloped with all his might, but arrived just too late.

III.—THE WIND AND THE SUN.

The Wind and the Sun disputed which was the more powerful, and agreed that he should be declared the victor who should first strip a traveller of his clothes. The Wind first tried his power, and blew with all his force. But the keener his blasts became, the more closely did the man wrap his cloak around him, till at last, resigning all hope, he called upon the Sun to see what he could do.

The Sun shone out with all his warmth. The traveller no sooner felt the genial rays than he began to take off one garment after another, till, at last, fairly overcome with heat, he undressed and bathed in a stream that lay in his path.

Exercises.

1. What lesson, do you think, is taught by each of these fables ?
2. Relate some fable that you know. Here are the titles of some well-known fables :—
   (a) The Fox and the Grapes.
   (b) The Dog in the Manger.
   (c) The Ass in the Lion's Skin.
   (d) The Lion and the Mouse.
   (e) The Dog and the Shadow.

The Barrel Organ.

(From "Collected Poems": Wm. Blackwood & Sons, by special permission of the Author and Publishers.)

Go down to Kew in lilac-time, in lilac-time, in lilac-time,
Go down to Kew in lilac-time (it isn't far from London !).
And you shall wander hand in hand with love in summer's wonderland ;
Go down to Kew in lilac-time (it isn't far from London !).

The cherry trees are seas of bloom and soft perfume and sweet perfume,
The cherry trees are seas of bloom (and oh ! so near to London !) ;
And there, they say, when dawn is high, and all the world 's a blaze of sky,
The cuckoo, though he 's very shy, will sing a song for London.

Kew Gardens in Spring (page 51)

The nightingale is rather rare, and yet they say you 'll
    hear him there,
At Kew, at Kew, in lilac-time (and oh! so near
    to London!);
The linnet and the throstle, too, and after dark the
    long halloo,
And golden-eyed tu-whit, tu-whoo of owls that
    ogle London.

For Noah hardly knew a bird of any kind that isn't
    heard
At Kew, at Kew, in lilac-time (and oh! so near to
    London!);
And when the rose begins to pout, and all the chest-
    nut spires are out,
You 'll hear the rest without a doubt, all chorusing
    for London.

Come down to Kew in lilac-time, in lilac-time, in
    lilac-time,
Come down to Kew in lilac-time (it isn't far from
    London!);
And you shall wander hand in hand with love in
    summer's wonderland.
Come down to Kew in lilac-time (it isn't far from
    London!).

Alfred Noyes.

How Tom Sawyer Whitewashed a Fence.

(From "Tom Sawyer," by Mark Twain, by special permission of
Messrs. Chatto & Windus.)

Saturday morning was come, and all the summer
world was bright and fresh and brimming with
life. There was song in every heart ; and if the
heart was young the music issued at the lips. There
was cheer in every face, and a spring in every step.
The locust trees were in bloom, and the fragrance
of the blossoms filled the air.

Cardiff Hill, beyond the village and above it, was
green with vegetation, and it lay just far enough
away to seem a Delectable Land, dreamy, reposeful,
inviting.

But Tom had got home pretty late the previous
night, and when his aunt saw the state his clothes
were in, she had made a firm resolution to turn his
Saturday holiday into a day of captivity.

After breakfast, Tom appeared on the side-walk
with a bucket of whitewash and a long-handled
brush. He surveyed the fence, and the gladness
went out of nature, and a deep melancholy settled
down upon his spirit. Thirty yards of broad fence
nine feet high ! It seemed to him that life was hollow,
and existence but a burden. Sighing, he dipped

his brush and passed it along the topmost plank: repeated the operation: did it again: compared the insignificant whitewashed streak with the far-reaching continent of unwhitewashed fence, and sat down on a tree-box discouraged. Jim came skipping out at the gate with a tin pail, and singing " Buffalo Gals." Bringing water from the town pump had always been hateful work in Tom's eyes before, but now it did not strike him so. He remembered that there was company at the pump. White, mulatto, and negro boys and girls were always there waiting their turns, resting, trading playthings, quarrelling, fighting, skylarking. And he remembered that although the pump was only a hundred and fifty yards off, Jim never got back with a bucket of water under an hour; and even then somebody generally had to go after him. Tom said: "Say, Jim; I'll fetch the water if you 'll whitewash some." Jim shook his head, and said:

"Can't, Ma'rs Tom. Ole missis she tole me I got to go an' git dis water an' not stop foolin' 'roun wid anybody. She say she spec' Ma'rs Tom gwyne to ax me to whitewash, an' so she tole me go 'long an' 'tend to my own business—she 'lowed she 'd 'tend to de whitewashin'."

"Oh, never you mind what she said, Jim. That 's the way she always talks. Gimme the bucket—I won't be gone only a minute. She won't ever know."

"Oh, I darn't, Ma'rs Tom. Ole missis she 'd take an' tar de head off'n me. 'Deed she would."

D

" She ! She never licks anybody—whacks 'em over
the head with her thimble, and who cares for that,
I 'd like to know ? She talks awful, but talk don't
hurt—anyways, it don't if she don't cry. Jim, I 'll
give you a marble. I 'll give you a white alley ! "

Jim began to waver.

" White alley, Jim : and it 's a bully tow."

" My ! dat 's a mighty gay marvel, *I* tell you.
But, Ma'rs Tom, I 's powerful 'fraid ole missis."

But Jim was only human—this attraction was
too much for him. He put down his pail, took the
white alley. In another minute he was flying down
the street with his pail, Tom was whitewashing
with vigour, and Aunt Polly was retiring from the
field with a slipper in her hand and triumph in her eye.

But Tom's energy did not last. He began to think
of the fun he had planned for the day, and his sorrows
multiplied. Soon the free boys would come tripping along on all sorts of delicious expeditions, and
they would make a world of fun of him for having
to work—the very thought of it burnt him like fire.
He got out his worldly wealth and examined it—
bits of toys, marbles, and trash : enough to buy an
exchange of work maybe, but not enough to buy so
much as half-an-hour of pure freedom. So he
returned his straitened means to his pocket, and
gave up the idea of trying to buy the boys. At this
dark and hopeless moment an inspiration burst
upon him, nothing less than a great magnificent
inspiration. He took up his brush and went tranquilly

to work. Ben Rogers hove in sight presently ; the very boy of all boys whose ridicule he had been dreading. Ben's gait was the hop, skip, and jump—proof enough that his heart was light and his anticipations high. He was eating an apple, and giving a long, melodious whoop at intervals, followed by a deep-toned ding dong dong, ding dong dong, for he was personating a steamboat. As he drew near he slackened speed, took the middle of the street, leaned far over to starboard, and rounded-to ponderously, and with laborious pomp and circumstance, for he was personating the Big Missouri, and considered himself to be drawing nine feet of water. He was boat, and captain, and engine-bells combined, so he had to imagine himself standing on his own hurricane-deck, giving the orders, and executing them.

"Stop her, sir ! Ling-a-ling-ling." The head-way ran almost out, and he drew up slowly toward the side-walk. "Ship up to back ! Ling-a-ling-ling !" His arms straightened and stiffened down his sides. "Let her back on the stabboard ! Ling-a-ling-ling ! Chow ! ch-chow-wow-chow !" his right hand meantime describing stately circles, for it was representing a forty-foot wheel. "Let her go back on the labboard ! Come ahead on the stabboard ! Stop her ! Let your outside turn over slow ! Ling-a-ling-ling ! Chow-ow-ow ! Get out that headline ! lively, now ! Come—out with your springline—what 're you about there ? Take a turn round that stump with the bight of it ! Stand by that stage now—let her go ! Done with the engines, sir ! Ling-a-ling-ling ! ''

" Sht ! s'sht ! sht ! '' (Trying the gauge-cocks.)

Tom went on whitewashing—paid no attention to the steamer. Ben stared a moment, and then said :

" Hi-yi ! You 're up a stump, ain't you ? ''

No answer. Tom surveyed his last brush with the eye of an artist, then he gave his brush another gentle sweep, and surveyed the result as before. Ben ranged up alongside of him. Tom's mouth watered for the apple, but he stuck to his work. Ben said :

" Hello, old chap ! you got to work, hey ? ''

" Why, it 's you, Ben ! I warn't noticing.''

" Say, I 'm going in a-swimming. I am. Don't you wish you could ? But, of course, you'd ruther work. Wouldn't you ? 'Course you would ! ''

Tom contemplated the boy a bit, and said :

" What do you call work ? ''

" Why, ain't that work ? ''

Tom resumed his whitewashing, and answered carelessly :

" Well, maybe it is, and maybe it ain't. All I know is, it suits Tom Sawyer.''

" Oh, come now, you don't mean to let on that you like it ? ''

The brush continued to move.

" Like it ? Well, I don't see why I oughn't to like

it. Does a boy get a chance to whitewash a fence every day ? "

That put the thing in a new light. Ben stopped nibbling his apple. Tom swept his brush daintily back and forth—stepped back to note the effect— added a touch here and there—contrasted the effect again, Ben watching every move, and getting more and more interested, more and more absorbed. Presently he said :

" Say, Tom, let me whitewash a little."

Tom considered : was about to consent : but he altered his mind :

" No, no : I reckon it wouldn't hardly do, Ben. You see, Aunt Polly 's awful particular about this fence—right here in the street, you know—but if it was the back fence I wouldn't mind, and she wouldn't. Yes, she 's awful particular about this fence ; it 's got to be done very careful : I reckon there ain't one boy in a thousand, maybe two thousand, that can do it the way it 's got to be done."

" No—is that so ? Oh, come now ; lemme just try, only just a little. I 'd let you, if you was me, Tom."

" Ben, I 'd like to, honest injun : but Aunt Polly —well, Jim wanted to do it, but she wouldn't let him. Sid wanted to do it, but she wouldn't let Sid. Now, don't you see how I 'm fixed ? If you was to tackle this fence, and anything was to happen to it——"

The retired artist sat in the shade (page 61).

"Oh, shucks, I 'll be just as careful. Now lemme try. Say—I 'll give you the core of my apple."

"Well, here. No, Ben; now don't; I 'm afeard ——"

"I 'll give you all of it."

Tom gave up the brush with reluctance in his face, but alacrity in his heart. And while the late steamer Big Missouri worked and sweated in the sun, the retired artist sat on a barrel in the shade close by, dangled his legs, munched his apple, and planned the slaughter of more innocents. There was no lack of material; boys happened along every little while; they came to jeer, but remained to whitewash. By the time Ben was fagged out Tom had traded the next chance to Billy Fisher for a kite in good repair; and when he played out, Johnny Miller bought in for a dead rat and a string to swing it with; and so on, and so on, hour after hour. And when the middle of the afternoon came, from being a poor, poverty-stricken boy in the morning, Tom was literally rolling in wealth. He had, besides the things I have mentioned, twelve marbles, part of a jew's harp, a piece of blue bottle-glass to look through, a spool-cannon, a key that wouldn't un-lock anything, a fragment of chalk, a glass stopper of a decanter, a tin soldier, a couple of tadpoles, six fire-crackers, a kitten with only one eye, a brass door-knob, a dog-collar—but no dog—the handle of a knife, four pieces of orange-peel and a dilapi-dated old window-sash. He had had a nice, good.

idle time all the while—plenty of company—and the
fence had three coats of whitewash on it ! If he
hadn't run out of whitewash, he would have bank-
rupted every boy in the village.

Exercises.
I.
1. Why did Tom dislike whitewashing the fence on
   a Saturday morning ?
2. How did Tom succeed in persuading his companions to do his work for him ?
3. In what part of the world do you think that this
   event took place ? Give a reason for your
   answer.
4. What did Ben Rogers imagine himself to be ?
5. What happened to Jim when he began to whitewash ?

II.
Find suitable words to go with the following
   words :—
   [Model : friend—*faithful* friend.]
   (a) Holiday, fence, expedition, afternoon, village,
   tunnel.
   [Model : glowing—glowing *furnace*.]
   (b) Magnificent, hollow, careless, particular,
   dreadful, generous.

III.
1. Tell this story in your own words.
2. Imagine yourself to be Ben Rogers, and give
   your account of what happened.
3. Describe the picture on p. 37.

THE WINDMILL

(By special permission of the Author and of the Publisher—
Mr. John Murray, London.)

The green corn waving in the dale,
The ripe grass waving on the hill :
I lean across the paddock pale
And gaze upon the giddy mill.

Beside his sacks the miller stands
On high within the open door :
A book and pencil in his hands,
His grist and meal he reckoneth o'er.

His tireless merry slave the wind
Is busy with his work to-day :
From whencesoe'er, he comes to grind ;
He hath a will and knows the way.

He gives the creaking sails a spin,
The circling millstones faster flee,
The shuddering timbers groan within,
And down the shoot the meal runs free.

The miller giveth him no thanks,
And doth not much his work o'erlook :
He stands beside the sacks, and ranks
The figures in his dusty book.

Robert Bridges.

The Story of Theseus.

(Abridged from Kingsley's "The Heroes.")

I.—HOW THESEUS LIFTED THE STONE.

Once upon a time there was a Princess who had
one fair son named Theseus. When Theseus was
eighteen years old, she took him up with her to the
temple of Poseidon, and into the thickets of the grove
which grew in the temple-yard. And there she
said : " Theseus, my son, go into that thicket, and
you will find at the foot of a plane tree a great flat
stone : lift it, and bring me what lies underneath."

Theseus pushed his way in through the thick bushes, and saw that they had not been moved for many a year. And, searching among their roots, he found a great flat stone, all overgrown with ivy and moss. He stood over the stone and tugged at it, and because his strength was very great, he was able to move it.

When he looked beneath it, on the ground lay a sword of bronze, with a hilt of glittering gold, and by it a pair of golden sandals; he caught them up and burst through the bushes like a wild boar, and leapt to his mother, holding them high above his head.

When she saw them, she said, " Come with me, Theseus, my son, where we can look down upon the sea."

Then they went and looked over the bright, blue sea towards Attica, where the Athenian people dwelt. And she said :

" That is a fair land and large, Theseus, my son, and it looks toward the sunny south ; a land of olive-oil and honey, the joy of gods and men. For the gods have girdled it with mountains, whose veins are of pure silver, and their bones of marble white as snow ; and there the hills are sweet with thyme, and the meadows with violets and asphodel, and the nightingales sing all night in the thickets by the side of everflowing streams. There are twelve towns well-peopled, the homes of an ancient race. What would you do, Theseus, if you were king of such a land ? "

Then Theseus' heart grew great within him, and he said :

" If I were king of such a land, I would rule it wisely and well in wisdom and in might, that when I died men might weep over my tomb, and cry ' Alas for the shepherd of his people ! ' "

Then she told him that Ægeus, king of Athens, was his father, and that Ægeus had treated her shamefully and had driven her forth from his house. When she had finished, she kissed her son, and wept over him, and went into the temple. And Theseus saw her no more.

II.—HOW THESEUS SLEW THE DEVOURERS OF MEN.

So Theseus stood there alone, with his mind full of many hopes. And first he thought of going down to the harbour and hiring a swift ship, and sailing across the bay to Athens ; but even that seemed too slow for him, and he longed for wings to fly across the sea, and find his father. But after a while his heart began to fail him, and he sighed, and said within himself :

" What if my father have other sons about him whom he loves ? He has forgotten me ever since I was born : why should he welcome me now ? "

Then he thought a long while sadly, and at last he cried aloud, " I will make him love me. I will win honour and renown. Did not Heracles win himself honour ? Where can I go, to do as Heracles did ? Where can I find strange adventures, robbers and monsters, and the enemies of men ? I will go by land, and into the mountains. Perhaps there I may hear of brave adventures, and do something which shall win my father's love."

So he went by land, and away into the mountains, with his father's sword upon his thigh. And he went up into the gloomy glens, between the furrowed marble cliffs, till the lowland grew blue beneath his feet, and the clouds drove damp about his head.

He went ever up and up, till he came to a pile of stones. And on the stones a man was sitting, wrapt in a bear-skin cloak. The head of a bear served him for a cap, and its teeth grinned white around his brows ; and the feet were tied about his throat, and their claws shone white upon his chest. And when he saw Theseus he rose, and laughed till the glens rattled.

"And who are you, fair fly," he asked, "who have walked into the spider's web ? Come hither and let me feast upon you, for these glens are the web from which no fly ever finds its way out again, and I am the spider who sucks the flies."

But Theseus came on steadily, and asked—

"And what is your name among men, bold spider ? and where are your spider's fangs ?"

Then the strange man said :

"Men call me Corynetes the club-bearer ; and here is my spider's fang." As he spoke he lifted from off the stone a mighty club of bronze. But

Theseus wrapt his mantle round his left arm quickly, in hard folds, and drew his sword, and rushed upon Corynetes, and Corynetes rushed on him.

Thrice he struck at Theseus, and made him bend under the blows like a sapling. And thrice Theseus sprang upright after the blow, and he stabbed at the club-bearer with his sword, but the loose folds of the bear-skin saved him.

Then Theseus grew mad, and closed with him, and caught him by the throat, and they fell and rolled over together; but when Theseus rose up from the ground, the club-bearer lay still and dead at his feet.

Theseus took his bear-skin and went on till he came to a pleasant fountain, where, under the shade of rocks and trees, nymphs and shepherds were dancing. They told him that, if he travelled farther, he would find Sinis the robber, who bent down two pine trees and bound all travellers hand and foot between them, and when he let the trees go again their bodies were torn asunder. "And after that," said one, "you must meet Sciron the robber, who will make you wash his feet, and while you are washing them, he will kick you over the cliff to the tortoise who lives below and feeds upon the bodies of the dead."

But he went on nevertheless, and in a pinewood he met Sinis, where the road ran between high rocks. There he sat by the wayside, with a young fir-tree for a club across his knees, and a cord laid ready by his side; and over his head, upon the fir tops, hung the bodies of murdered men.

Then Theseus shouted to him: "Valiant pine-bender, hast thou two fir-trees left for me?"

THESEUS

"Their bodies were torn asunder."

And Sinis leapt to his feet, and rushed on Theseus, lifting up his club, and Theseus rushed upon him.

Then they hammered together till the green woods rang: but the metal was tougher than the pine, and Sinis' club broke right across, as the bronze came down upon it. Then Theseus smote Sinis down upon his face, and knelt upon his back, and bound him with his own cord, and said: "As thou hast done to others, so shall it be done to thee."

Then he bent down two young fir-trees, and bound Sinis between them, for all his struggling and his prayers ; and he let them go, and went on, leaving Sinis to the hawks and crows.

After that he went on, till he found Sciron on a narrow path between the mountain and the sea. On his knees was a mighty club ; and he had barred the path with stones.

Then Theseus shouted to him, and said : " Tortoise-feeder, do thy feet need washing to-day ? "

And Sciron leapt to his feet, and answered :

" My tortoise is hungry, and my feet need washing to-day."

Then Theseus rushed upon him ; and sore was the battle upon the cliff, for when Sciron felt the weight of the bronze club, he dropped his own, and closed with Theseus, and tried to hurl him by main force over the cliff. But Theseus was a wary wrestler, and caught him by the throat and by the knee, and forced him against the wall till it fell, and Sciron rolled head over heels.

Then Theseus lifted him up all bruised, and drew his sword, and sat down by the well, and said : " Come hither, and wash my feet, or I will cut you piece-meal."

And Sciron washed his feet trembling, and, when it was done, Theseus rose and cried : " As thou hast done to others, so shall it be done to thee. Go, feed thy tortoise thyself ; " and he kicked him over the cliff into the sea.

From there Theseus went a long day's journey towards Attica, and as he was skirting the vale of Cephissus a very tall and strong man came down to meet him, dressed in rich garments. On his arms were golden bracelets, and round his neck a collar of jewels; and he came forward, bowing courteously, and held out both his hands, and spoke—

"Welcome, fair youth, to these mountains; happy am I to have met you! For what greater pleasure to a good man than to entertain strangers? But I see that you are weary. Come to my castle and rest yourself awhile. Come up with me, and eat venison, and drink the rich red wine, and sleep upon my famous bed, of which all travellers say that they never saw the like. For whatsoever the stature of my guest, however tall or short, that bed fits him to a hair, and he sleeps upon it as he never slept before." And he laid hold on Theseus' hands, and would not let him go.

Theseus wished to go forward; but he was ashamed to seem churlish to so hospitable a man: and he was curious to see that wondrous bed, and, beside, he was hungry and weary; yet he shrank from the man, he knew not why; for, though his voice was fawning, it was dry and husky like a toad's; and though his eyes were gentle, they were dull and cold like stones. But he consented, and went with the man up the glen, under the dark shadow of the cliffs.

And as they went up, narrower grew the glen, and higher and darker the cliffs, and beneath them

E

a torrent roared, half seen between bare limestone
crags, and around them was neither tree nor bush,
while from the peaks snow-blasts swept down, cutting and chilling, till a horror fell on Theseus as
he looked round at that doleful place. And he said
at last : " Your castle stands, it seems, in a dreary
region."

" Yes," answered the stranger, " but, once within
it, hospitality makes all things cheerful. But who
are these ? " and he looked back, and Theseus also ;
and, far below, along the road which they had left,
came a string of asses, and merchants walking
beside them.

" Ah, poor souls ! " said the tall man. " Well
for them that I saw them ! Wait awhile till I go down
and call them, and we will eat and drink together."

And he ran back down the hill, waving his hand
and shouting to the merchants, while Theseus went
slowly up the steep pass.

But as he went up he met an aged man, who had
been gathering driftwood in the torrent bed. He
had laid down his faggot on the road, and was trying
to lift it again to his shoulder. And when he saw
Theseus he called to him, and said—

" O fair youth, help me up with my burden, for
my limbs are stiff and weak with years."

Then Theseus lifted the burden on his own back.
And the old man blessed him, and then looked
earnestly upon him, and said—

" Who are you, fair youth, and wherefore travel

you this doleful road?" And Theseus answered: "I travel this doleful road because I have been invited by a hospitable man, who promises to feast me, and to make me sleep upon a wondrous bed."

Then the old man cried: "Know, fair youth, that you are going to torment and to death, for he who met you is a robber and a murderer of men. Whatsoever stranger he meets he entices hither to death, and as for this bed of which he speaks, truly it fits all comers, yet none ever rose alive off it save me."

"Why?" asked Theseus, astonished.

"Because, if a man be too tall for it, he lops his limbs till they be short enough, and, if he be too short, he stretches his limbs till they be long enough; but one only he spared, seven weary years agone: for I alone of all filled his bed exactly, so he spared me, and made me his slave. And once I was a wealthy merchant, and dwelt in brazen-gated Thebes; but now I hew wood and draw water for him, the torment of all mortal men. And, therefore, is he called Procrustes the Stretcher. Flee from him. Yet whither will you flee? The cliffs are steep, and who can climb them? and there is no other road."

Then Theseus ground his teeth together, and laid his hands upon the old man's mouth, and said: "There is no need to flee;" and he turned to go down the pass.

"Do not tell him that I have warned you, or he will kill me by some evil death," the old man screamed after him down the glen ; but Theseus strode on in his wrath.

Soon he met Procrustes coming up the hill, and all the merchants with him smiling and talking gaily. And when he saw Theseus, he cried : " Ah, fair young guest, have I kept you too long waiting ? "

But Theseus answered sternly : " The man who stretches his guests upon a bed and hews off their hands and feet, what shall be done to him, when right is done throughout the land ? "

Then Procrustes' countenance changed, and his cheeks grew green as a lizard, and he felt for his sword in haste. But Theseus leapt upon him, and clasped him round waist and elbow, so that he could not draw his sword, and flung him from him, and lifted up his dreadful club, and before the robber could strike him he had struck, and Procrustes' evil soul fled forth, and went down to Hades squeaking, like a bat into the darkness of a cave.

Then Theseus stript him of his gold ornaments, and went up to his house, and found there great wealth and treasure, which he had stolen from the passers-by. And he called the people of the country, and parted the spoil among them, and went down the mountains, and away.

And he went down the slopes of oak, through mist and rain, till he saw the plain of Athens, and the hill where Athene dwells. And all the people ran out to meet him ; for his fame had gone before him, and everyone knew of his mighty deeds. So he went to Ægeus' palace, and stood on the threshold; and a servant ran and told Ægeus. So Ægeus came out, and when Theseus saw him, his heart leapt into his mouth, and he cast himself upon his father's neck, and wept, and told him who he was.

III.

HOW THESEUS SLEW THE MINOTAUR.

So Theseus stayed with his father all the winter; and when the spring drew near, all the Athenians grew sad and silent, and Theseus saw it, and asked the reason; but no one would answer him a word. He went to his father, and asked him; Ægeus turned away his face and wept, and at last he said:

"Do not ask me, my son, beforehand, about evils which must happen: it is enough to have to face them when they come."

When the day equals the night in length, a herald came to Athens and stood in the market-place, and cried: "O people and king of Athens, where is your yearly tribute?" Then a great lamentation arose throughout the city. But Theseus stood up and cried: "Who are you, dog-faced, who dare demand tribute here? If I did not reverence your herald's staff, I would slay you with this club."

And the herald answered proudly, for he was a grave and ancient man: "Fair youth, I am not dog-faced or shameless: but I do the bidding of my master, Minos, the King of hundred-citied Crete,

the wisest of all kings on earth. You must surely
be a stranger here, or you would know why I come,
and that I come by right."

"I am a stranger here. Tell me, then, why you
are come," replied Theseus.

"To fetch the tribute," answered the herald,
"which King Ægeus promised to Minos. For Minos
conquered all this land when he came hither with a
great fleet of ships, enraged about the murder of
his son. For Androgeus, his son, came hither and
overcame all the Greeks in the sports, so that the
people honoured him as a hero. But when Ægeus
saw his valour he envied him, and feared lest he
should take away the sceptre from him. Therefore
he plotted against his life, and slew him basely. So
Minos came and avenged him, and would not depart
till the land had promised him tribute—seven youths
and seven maidens every year, who go with me in
a black-sailed ship, till they come to hundred-citied
Crete."

Theseus went to his father, and asked him about
the matter. But Ægeus turned away his head, and
said : "Blood was shed in the land unjustly, and
by blood it is avenged. Break not my heart by questions : it is enough to endure in silence."

Then Theseus groaned inwardly, and said : "I
will go myself with these youths and maidens, and
kill Minos upon his royal throne."

And Ægeus shrieked, and cried : "You shall not
go. You shall not go, my son, the light of my old

age, to whom alone I look to rule this people after I am dead. You shall not go, to die horribly, as these youths and maidens die : for Minos thrusts them into a labyrinth, from whence no one can escape, entangled in its winding mazes, before he meets the Minotaur, the monster who feeds upon the flesh of men. There he devours them horribly, and they never see this land again."

Theseus grew red, and his ears tingled, and his heart beat loud in his bosom. And he stood awhile like a tall stone pillar on the cliffs above some hero's grave, and at last he spoke :

"Therefore, all the more will I go with them, and slay the accursed beast. Have I not slain Corynetes, and Sinis, and Sciron, and Procrustes?"

When he heard that, Ægeus cried : "But how will you slay him, my son? For you must leave your club and your armour behind, and be cast defenceless and naked to the monster."

And Theseus said : "Are there no stones in that labyrinth, and have I not my hands?"

Then Ægeus clung to his knees, and at last, weeping bitterly, said : "Promise me but this. If you return in peace, though that may hardly be, take down the black sail of the ship (for I shall watch for it every day upon the cliffs), and hoist instead a white sail, that I may know afar off that you are safe."

And Theseus promised and went to where the herald stood, while they drew lots for the youths and maidens, and he cried :

" There is one who needs no lot. I will be one
of the seven."

So they went down to the black-sailed ship, seven
maidens and seven youths, and Theseus before them
all, and the people followed them lamenting. But
Theseus whispered to his companions : " Have hope,
for the monster is not immortal." Then their hearts
were comforted a little. But they wept as they went
on board, and the cliffs of Sunium rang, and all the
isles of the Ægean Sea, with the voice of their wailing
as they sailed towards Crete.

At last they came to Crete and to Cnossus, beneath
the peaks of Ida, and to the palace of Minos the great
king, to whom Zeus himself taught laws. So he
was the wisest of all mortal kings. His ships were
as many as the seagulls, and his palace was like
a marble hill. Theseus came to where Minos sat
among the pillars of the hall, upon his throne of
beaten gold, and stood before him, and they looked
each other in the face. And Minos bade take them
to the prison, and cast them to the monster one by
one. Then Theseus cried : " A boon, O Minos !
Let me be thrown first to the beast. For I am the
son of him whom of all men thou hatest most, Ægeus
King of Athens, and I am come here of my own will,
to end this matter."

And Minos pondered awhile, looking steadfastly
upon him, and he thought : " This youth seems to
atone by his own death for his father's sin."

Then they led Theseus into the prison, with the

other youths and maids. But Ariadne, Minos'
daughter, saw him, as she came out of her white
stone hall, and she loved him for his courage and
his majesty, and said : " Shame that such a youth
should die ! " And by night she went down to the
prison and told him all her heart ; and said :

" Flee down to your ship at once, for I have bribed
the guards before the doors. Flee, you and all your
friends, and go back in peace to Greece ; and take
me, take me with you ! for I dare not stay after you
are gone : for my father will kill me miserably, if he
knows what I have done."

And Theseus stood silent awhile ; for he was
astonished and confounded by her beauty : but at
last he said : " I cannot go home in peace till I have
seen and slain the Minotaur, and avenged the deaths
of the youths and maidens, and put an end to the
terrors of my land."

Then she loved him all the more, and said :

" Fair youth, you are too bold : but I can help
you, weak as I am. I will give you a sword, and
with that perhaps you may slay the beast ; and a
clue of thread, and by that, perhaps, you may find
your way out again. Only promise me that if you
escape safe you will take me home with you to Greece ;
for my father will surely kill me, if he knows what
I have done."

Then Theseus laughed, and said : " Am I not
safe enough now ? " And he hid the sword in his
bosom, and rolled up the clue in his hand ; and then

he pledged his faith to Ariadne, and fell down before
her, and kissed her hands and her feet : and she
wept over him a long while, and then went away ;
and Theseus lay down and slept sweetly.

And when evening came, the guards came in and
led him away to the labyrinth.

And he went down into that doleful gulf, through
winding paths among the rocks, under caverns, and
arches, and galleries, and over heaps of fallen stone.
And he turned on the left hand, and on the right
hand, and went up and down, till his head was dizzy ;
but all the while he held his clue. For when he went
in he had fastened it to a stone, and left it to unroll
out of his hand as he went on ; and it lasted him
till he met the Minotaur, in a narrow chasm between
black cliffs.

And when he saw him he stopped awhile, for he
had never seen so strange a beast. His body was
a man's ; but his head was the head of a bull : and
his teeth were the teeth of a lion ; and with them
he tore his prey. And when he saw Theseus he
roared, and put his head down, and rushed right
at him.

But Theseus stept aside nimbly, and as he passed
by cut him in the knee ; and ere he could turn in
the narrow path he followed him and stabbed him
again and again from behind, till the monster fled
bellowing wildly, for he never before had felt a wound.
And Theseus followed him at full speed, holding
the clue of thread in his left hand.

Theseus met the Minotaur in a narrow chasm between black **cliffs**.

Then on, through cavern after cavern, under dark ribs of sounding stone, and up rough glens and torrent beds, among the sunless rocks of Ida, and to the edge of the eternal snow, went they, the hunter and the hunted, while the hills bellowed to the monster's bellow.

And at last Theseus came up with him, where he lay panting on a slab among the snow, and caught him by the horns, and forced his head back, and drove the keen sword through his throat.

Then he turned, and went back limping and weary, feeling his way down by the clue of thread, till he came to the mouth of that doleful place, and saw Ariadne waiting for him.

And he whispered : " It is done ! " and showed her the sword ; and she laid her finger on her lips, and led him to the prison, and opened the doors, and set all the prisoners free, while the guards lay sleeping heavily, for she had silenced them with wine.

Then they fled to their ship together, and leapt on board, and hoisted the sail ; and through the glimmering night they escaped all safe to Naxos, where Ariadne became Theseus' wife.

But she never came to Athens with her husband. Some say that Theseus left her at Naxos, and others that he was driven from her. But, however that may be, in his haste or his grief, Theseus forgot to put up the white sail. Now Ægeus, his father, had sat and watched on Cape Sunium day after day, and had strained his old eyes across the sea to descry the ship afar. And when he saw the black sail, and not the white, he gave up Theseus for dead, and in his grief he fell into the sea and died; so it is called the Ægean Sea to this day.

And now Theseus was King of Athens, and he guarded the land, and ruled it well.

R. EADIE

Exercises.

I.

1. What did Theseus find beneath the stone?
2. What did Theseus answer when his mother asked him how he would rule if he should become king?

3. Why did Theseus choose the rough and dangerous mountain road to Attica ?
4. Make a list of the adventures which Theseus met with on his journey.
5. What was the tribute which Ægeus had to pay to Minos ?
6. Why had he to pay this tribute ?
7. What was the promise made to his father by Theseus, when he set sail for Crete ?
8. What was the boon which Theseus craved of King Minos ?
9. By what means did Ariadne aid Theseus to kill the Minotaur and escape from the labyrinth ?
10. Why is the Ægean Sea called by that name ?

II.

Write sentences describing the following :—The land of Attica, Corynetes, Procrustes, The Minotaur, Minos, The Labyrinth.

III.

1. Relate the story of Procrustes.
2. Describe the death of the Minotaur.
3. Retell the following story at greater length and complete it in the way you think best :—

There once lived a girl whose name was Arachne, who was very clever at spinning and weaving. The goddess Minerva admired her work very greatly, but was offended when she heard Arachne boast that no one could equal her. Accordingly Minerva challenged Arachne to a trial of skill. . . . Thus was Arachne punished for her pride.

Lochinvar.

O, young Lochinvar is come out of the west!
Through all the wide Border his steed was the best,
And save his good broad-sword he weapons had none ;
He rode all unarmed and he rode all alone.
So faithful in love, and so dauntless in war,
There never was knight like the young Lochinvar.

He stayed not for brake, and he stopped not for stone,
He swam the Esk river where ford there was none ;
But, ere he alighted at Netherby gate,
The bride had consented, the gallant came late :
For a laggard in love, and a dastard in war,
Was to wed the fair Ellen of brave Lochinvar.

So boldly he entered the Netherby hall
Among bride's-men and kinsmen, and brothers and
    all :
Then spoke the bride's father, his hand on his sword
(For the poor craven bridegroom said never a word),
" O come ye in peace here, or come ye in war,
Or to dance at our bridal, young Lord Lochinvar ? "

" I long wooed your daughter, my suit you denied :—
Love swells like the Solway, but ebbs like its tide—

And now I am come, with the lost love of mine,
To lead but one measure, drink one cup of wine.
There are maidens in Scotland more lovely by far,
That would gladly be bride to the young Lochinvar.''

The bride kissed the goblet; the knight took it up,
He quaffed off the wine, and he threw down the cup,
She looked down to blush, and she looked up to
     sigh,
With a smile on her lips and a tear in her eye.
He took her soft hand, ere her mother could bar,—
'' Now tread we a measure ! '' said young Lochinvar.

So stately his form, and so lovely her face,
That never a hall such a galliard did grace;
While her mother did fret, and her father did fume,
And the bridegroom stood dangling his bonnet and
     plume ;
And the bride-maidens whispered, '' 'Twere better
     by far
To have matched our fair cousin with young Loch-
     invar.''

One touch to her hand, and one word in her ear,
When they reached the hall-door, and the charger
     stood near ;

So light to the croupe the fair lady he swung,
So light to the saddle before her he sprung!
"She is won! we are gone, over bark, bush, and
    scaur;
They 'll have fleet steeds that follow," quoth young
    Lochinvar.

F

There was mounting 'mong Graemes of the Netherby
    clan ;
Forsters, Fenwicks, and Musgraves, they rode and
    they ran,
There was racing, and chasing, on Cannobie Lee,
But the lost bride of Netherby ne'er did they see.
So daring in love, and so dauntless in war,
Have ye e'er heard of gallant like young Lochinvar ?

Sir Walter Scott.

Exercises.
I.
Find words which rhyme with
    (a) ear, plume, gate, mine, face, west.
    (b) sky, life, night, glow, wing, meet.

II.
1. Tell in your own words the story contained in
    this poem ; or
2. Tell this story, imagining yourself to be the bride's
    mother, or younger brother.

The Dragon Fly

Have you ever visited the haunts of the Dragon Fly, the largest and swiftest insect that inhabits this country? If not, come with me, and let us find out, this hot summer day, some stream which runs slowly along a valley, with rich green meadows on both sides, in which, here and there, a pond is situated. This is such a spot as the dragon fly will choose for laying its eggs, and here the full-grown fly spends its brief life of four or five months. As the sun is shining we shall hope to see many of these gaily-coloured insects darting hither and thither in search of prey. We will arm ourselves with a butter-fly net, a dredging net, and a glass jar, in the hope of capturing some specimens.

Here we are! These trees to right and left leave a little open space of sunlight, and, sure enough, there is the object of our interest, with long, thin body coloured a bright blue, sailing to and fro, always returning over the same track, and making sudden side-flights when it spies some other insect on the wing. It takes no notice of us, for it does not know fear. It is too swift to be caught by a bird, and it is as completely lord over other insects as is the tiger over the smaller animals of the Indian jungle.

A white butterfly flits across its path. With a motion so rapid that the eye cannot follow it, it has seized the wretched victim in its forelegs. It continues its flight down the glade, its metallic wings flashing back the rays of the sun. The butterfly's legs and wings drop to the ground, and with its powerful jaws the fierce fly is biting at the body, still carrying it in the air.

To catch the creature in our net seems to be hopeless. It sees us approaching, and, although it disdains to depart altogether, it darts off each time the net sweeps towards it. Even when it settles it cannot be taken easily. We strike, and the net comes down on the tree-trunk where it was stationed, but the fly has already gone.

Now a passing cloud darkens the face of the sun for a time, and our chance has come. For the Dragon Fly needs the stimulus of scorching warmth to keep it active. In a few minutes we have found several on leaves, and among the reeds by the side of one of the ponds, and have caught them in the net, and transferred them to the glass jar we have brought with us. We can now examine one at leisure.

It has four long wings, each of which consists of a transparent membrane, exceedingly thin and looking like a net, because of the nervures. The wings are highly polished and glisten in the light.

They are very strong and rigid, and are moved by powerful muscles in the fly's back and sides.

Its six legs are not very remarkable. The Dragon Fly never walks, and its legs would not be serviceable for that purpose. They are used almost entirely for holding its prey, before the act of devouring has commenced.

A simple magnifying glass will help to display the smaller features of the body. Let us begin with the head.

This is large, and possesses formidable jaws. They cannot be seen at first, but if we give the fly a little bit of leaf, or an insect, we observe that it bites savagely and quickly. It has a pair of lips which move up and down, and cover its true biting jaws, which are like saws, and move sideways.

It has two large and brilliant compound eyes, each containing hundreds of facets. In addition, it has three simple eyes, on the front of its head. This generous supply of eyes reveals to us why we could not at first come near the fly, and why it darts so confidently and speedily after insects which are invisible to human sight. It is provided with means of both near and distant vision. The Dragon Fly, in fact, has very keen sight, and is endowed with the power of finding prey much as is the eagle among birds. Though diminutive in comparison with our-selves, it is, in truth, a terrible foe to other flies. Its wings are so powerful and its vision is so keen that it very rarely fails to strike its prey at the first dart.

The part behind the head, which is called the thorax, carries the wings. Next to this comes the slender and beautifully-marked abdomen. The abdomen of the specimens we have caught is blue. But there are many other species with differently-coloured abdomens, we perceive, and even in the same species the hue varies considerably. The abdomen is straight, as a rule. As we hold the insect by the thorax, however, between finger and thumb, it curls its abdomen round, in its effort to escape, as if it was trying to sting. But there is no need to be afraid. The abdomen is sharply-pointed, but it has no sting. The country people do not know this, and generally believe that the Dragon Fly inflicts a very painful sting; and, indeed, its movements are so quick and suggestive, and its habits so fierce, that we can well understand how the error arose.

Like other members of the same great family, it passes through remarkable changes of form. Most insects have four phases, the egg, the larva or grub, the chrysalis, and the perfect insect. The Dragon Fly has only three, for it omits the chrysalis stage. Let us return to the pond, to discover what we can about the earlier life of this wonderful insect.

Some of the flies that we had observed among the reeds had settled there for the purpose of laying eggs, which they do on, or just below, the surface of the water. Almost at any time in the year the larvae may be found in the mud at the bottom of the ponds. We select a likely spot, and, after a few attempts, secure a fine example.

It is a broad, flat creature coloured a dirty grey, so that it cannot be seen against the mud on which, or in which, it loves to lie. It does not often move about. It prefers to lurk half-buried, and to make a sudden spring upon its prey. The fly is a terror to insects in the air, and the larva is equally ferocious, devouring everything which it can seize.

Having put the larva into the jar with clean water we can observe it easily. Its head is large, and has two antennæ or feelers, and two prominent eyes. On the thorax are six strong legs, and two pairs of undeveloped wings. The abdomen, which is broad and flat, is divided into segments.

The best way to examine its habits of feeding is to introduce a few pond insects and larvae into the jar. See, there is an insect swimming near a larva! Suddenly, from the front of the face, a long arm furnished with claws shoots out and seizes the hapless victim in a vice-like grip. This arm is really the lower lip, and is known as the mask, because it covers the front of the head. Behind it are jaws similar to those possessed by the perfect insect. The prey is soon devoured and the larva settles down again. To stir it to activity we insert a stick in the water, intending to give it a gentle poke. But as soon as the stick approaches, the insect shoots forward without making, in appearance, any motion of its limbs. It accomplishes this movement by forcibly ejecting water from its tail. The larva remains in the water, from the time the egg is hatched till it emerges as the fly, for a period of nine or ten months. It is quite small at first, but grows with great rapidity, and it has an enormous appetite.

The final change, when the larva leaves the water, is most interesting to watch. As there are many flies about, and as the day is hot, we may hope, by good fortune, to find an opportunity of observing it. On the pond weeds we have seen one or two larvae. These are climbing upwards, and when they come above the surface they will wait to moult their old skins. Here is one. Its skin has dried and is beginning to split. The insect inside is wriggling from side to side. At last it gets its head and legs free, and begins to drag its abdomen slowly from the case. At last it is quite disengaged, and rests exhausted on the stem of the water plant to which its old coat is still clinging. It looks quite different from the flies we see around us; for its wings are creased and small, and its body is moist, and very soft.

But, by degrees, in the warm sun, it expands in every way. Its wings stretch and become stiff, its body straightens and hardens, and before long it moves its wings faster and faster till at last it is suddenly off, ready to begin its life of hunting, which, if it is fortunate, will continue until the cold of approaching winter puts an end to its existence.

Exercises.

I.

1. Into what three parts is the Dragon Fly's body divided ?

2. Describe the Dragon Fly's eyes.

3. What stages does a Dragon Fly pass through during the course of its life ?

4. How does the Dragon Fly larva catch its prey ?

5. Where are Dragon Flies most likely to be found ?

6. Where do Dragon Flies lay their eggs ?

7. What is the Dragon Fly like when it first emerges from its old case ?

8. Describe the larva of the Dragon Fly.

9. Why is a Dragon Fly hard to catch ?

II.

Make sentences containing the following words correctly used :—

(a) Savagely, remarkable, completely, powerful, scorching, brief, display, devour, supply, invisible, vision, transfer, emerge, forcibly, approach, hapless, victim, observe, different, prominent.

(b) Evergreen, refuse, hero, comical, monster, contented, scramble, miserable, excited, immediately, applause, combat, certain, lament, gallant, rescue, upright, reward, surprise.

III.

1. Describe any insect whose appearance and habits are known to you.

2. Describe the capture of a Gnat by a Spider.

3. Relate a conversation which is supposed to take place between a Dragon Fly and a Spider.

Norton Wood.

In Norton Wood the sun was bright,
In Norton Wood the air was light,
And meek anemones,
Kissed by the April breeze,
Were trembling left and right.
Ah, vigorous year!
Ah, primrose dear
With smile so arch!
Ah, budding larch!
Ah, hyacinth so blue,
We also must make free with you!
Where are those cowslips hiding?
But we should not be chiding—
The ground is covered every inch—
What sayest thou, master finch?
I see you on the swaying bough!
And very neat you are, I vow!
And Dora says it is " the happiest day! "
Her birthday, hers!
And there 's a jay,
And from that clump of firs
Shoots a great pigeon, purple, blue, and grey,
And, circling home,
Well laden, as we clomb
Sweet Walton hill
A cuckoo shouted with a will—
" Cuckoo! cuckoo! " the first we 've heard!
" Cuckoo! cuckoo! " God bless the bird!
Scarce time to take his breath,
And now " Cuckoo " he saith—
" Cuckoo! cuckoo! " three cheers!
And let the welkin ring!
He has not folded wing
Since last he saw Algiers.   *T. L. Brown.*

Norton Wood (page 96)

Twisting the Dragon's Tail.

On the night of April 22nd, 1918, a little fleet of grey war vessels slipped quietly out of their harbours on the south-east coast of England and headed for Belgium. Little would the anxious millions left behind on these shores have guessed, even if they had known of the departure, the dangerous errand on which the brave men who worked and manned the ships were bent, or with what patient skill their plans had been laid.

There were the "Vindictive," a light cruiser, which was to play a principal part; five larger and older cruisers; two ferryboats from the river Mersey, the "Iris" and the "Daffodil": a number of flat-bottomed ships called monitors, armed with enormous sixteen-inch guns; torpedoboat destroyers, and two submarines. Some of the big ships carried motor launches.

The leader of this strange fleet, Vice-Admiral Sir Roger Keyes, was on board the destroyer "Warwick": Captain Carpenter commanded the "Vindictive"; Lieutenant Sandford, Wing Commander Brock of the Royal Naval Air Force, and Lieutenant Rigby were there, besides many others whose names are worthy to be for ever famous in story for heroism and love of country.

For nearly four years the fury of the great war had raged. All the combatants were becoming exhausted, and, by land, by sea, and by air, the enemy was trying to bring Britain to her knees.

From Flanders the men on board could hear, booming over the waters every now and then, the noise of the artillery, which never slept, day or night. The foe was creeping daily nearer to the Channel. Gigantic attacks had recently been launched against the allied lines in northern France, before which the soldiers, fighting doggedly and contesting every inch of ground, were being steadily forced towards Calais and Boulogne. The slaughter on both sides was appalling, but still the Germans kept on.

The peril from the air, though perhaps not so deadly, was a severer trial of nerve for the non-combatants. In former wars the inhabitants of England had been comparatively secure in their island home. But now from the stations on the Continent airships and aeroplanes flew over the land far and wide, dropping bombs on the chief towns, and often killing and maiming defenceless women and little children. This abominable method of warfare aroused as much indignation as fear, and at last our air-defence became strong enough to defeat, and finally to ward off, the hostile aircraft.

The menace by sea was more serious. As the British nation depends for a large part of its food on supplies from foreign countries and from the colonies, the Germans hoped to starve us into defeat by preventing the food ships from carrying provisions to these shores. Their battleships and cruisers being

The "Vindictive" at the Mole (page 106)

shut up in their harbours by our fleet, they resorted to their submarines, which could come and go unseen and unexpected. Fleets of submarines prowled round the coast of Britain, sinking every vessel which they could catch, leaving the drowning seamen to their fate, and not seldom firing upon them when they took to the boats.

Great damage was done. Provisions grew scarcer, and prices rose. Meanwhile no effort seemed able to interfere with the piracy of the submarines, until at length men's patience began to give way, and they began to murmur that the British navy had forgotten its old traditions, and had lost the power of adventurous attack. It was the blackest moment of the war.

But those whose hearts were sinking were wrong. The darkest hour comes just before the dawn. In Flanders a few months later the French, American, and British armies were to rise in unmatched strength, and were to drive the foe headlong before them. The German navy was never to emerge from its hiding-place except to surrender. And against the submarines a blow was to be dealt with the fame of which the world would ring.

The spirit of Blake and Rodney, Nelson and Howe was still alive in the breasts of the sailors. Just as the Elizabethan sea-king sailed into the harbour of Cadiz and, by burning the King of Spain's ships, delayed the departure of the Spanish Armada, a twentieth century hero was to strike at the very heart of the enemy. Sir Roger Keyes had matured a plan by which he hoped to rid the seas of the plague with which they were infested, and it was to put the plan into execution that the little fleet, manned by 1,800 volunteers whom no peril could daunt, no difficulty defeat, set out so quietly on that memorable afternoon.

The fastnesses on the Belgian coast whence the destroying U-Boats issued, and whither they returned from their marauding cruises, were at Ostend and Zeebrugge. These two towns, which lie about a dozen miles apart, were both connected with Bruges by canals, so that on returning from an expedition a German submarine could retreat to a place of absolute security, quite out of the range of the guns of our ships. Inside these canals lay thirty-five torpedo craft and a fleet of about thirty submarines. The coastline between Ostend and Zeebrugge had been strongly fortified, for along its twelve miles were stationed no fewer than 225 heavy long-range guns.

The places where the canals meet the sea were defended by piers, each of which terminated in a lighthouse. At Zeebrugge it had been found necessary to protect the entrance from drifting sands by building a large crescent-shaped mole on the western side. This was about eighty yards wide, and a little less than a mile in length. The portion nearest to the shore consisted of a viaduct carrying a railway. At the end of the viaduct was a railway station.

The outer half of the work was a large breakwater holding store-sheds, and ending in another lighthouse. Numbers of machine guns were planted on the mole, it was strongly garrisoned, and on the coast around were placed a large number of heavy batteries.

For a hostile ship to approach such an array of artillery was to risk being blown out of the water. But, if the entrances to the canals could be blocked in any way, the submarines inside would be unable to come out, our own ports on the North Sea would be safe for our ships to use, and any submarines which the Germans wished to send to sea would have to come a much greater distance before they could attack the provision ships plying to England and Scotland.

Sir Roger Keyes decided to make the attempt, hazardous as it was. He decided to try to sink ships in the mouths of the canals. To accomplish this, it was necessary also to make an attack on the mole at Zeebrugge, for, otherwise, the machine gunners placed there would be able to sweep the decks of our ships with their bullets.

To be discovered would be fatal to success. Everything had to be done during the hours of darkness, and by surprise. A light and steady wind was needed to carry a smoke screen which the destroyers would provide to hide the movements of the ships. Unless the sky was overcast the aeroplanes of the enemy would quickly discover that mischief was afoot.

A sufficient depth of water had to be round the mole for the cruisers to lay to at its side. Therefore, the night of the attack had to be chosen with the utmost care.

Each man's duty was allotted beforehand, and every preparation was made. Twice the fleet had started, twice the weather had changed, and twice the ships had returned. At last the right moment came, and the ships got under weigh three hours before sunset. They had to reach Ostend at midnight, complete the operation before half-past one, and be back before daybreak should expose them as targets to the fire of the guns along the shore.

The evening was misty and a gentle rain was falling. We can imagine the feelings of the men who were about to enter the jaws of death in this attempt to serve or save their country. They knew full well that many of them were doomed never to see home again, that before many hours had passed perhaps all of them would rest in watery graves. Around them were floating mines which, if touched, would blow a hole in the side of the strongest ship and sink her. Down in the engine-rooms they toiled at the furnaces, above they stood to the guns. The men of the landing parties, armed with bombs, rifles and bayonets, thought of the desperate assault in which they were soon to share. Every heart beat high, for, though the risk was great, the glory would be greater, if success should crown their efforts.

Just before dark the sun broke out angry and red

below the clouds, shedding its last beams over the dull sea. The weather had worsened somewhat and the waves were higher, but no sign of a German plane had been observed. Then night came down. Without lights and with as little noise as possible the fleet approached the Belgian coast.

Let us take our stand on the heroic " Vindictive," which is due to reach the mole at midnight exactly. Captain Carpenter is on the bridge. All around is silent as the tomb. It is half-past eleven. Suddenly, the noise of a gun fired far on our right is heard ; it is followed by another, and another, and another. Soon all round us the roar of the cannonade re-echoes, for the monitors are bombarding the coast defences. In twenty minutes we shall have arrived, and the action will have begun. The inky darkness seems to thicken, and there is a choking smell in the air. The destroyers are stretching their screen of smoke over us.

Unfortunately, the wind changes, and the sky quickly clears. In front of us we can see the Belgian coast, stretching in both directions as a long, black line. Those who are watching on shore see us too. Instantly we are blinded by an intolerable radiance, which comes from a searchlight turned full on us. We are discovered !

Right above us a shell bursts, and five stars hang in the air, and float and gently descend. The night grows bright as midday. Then a terrific roar overwhelms our senses, mixed with sharp and deafening explosions which seem to be everywhere at once. The shore batteries have opened on us. Men fall and tackle snaps, and splinters sing drearily through the air, while tall columns of water rise on every side.

Behind us are two dark forms, the "Iris" and the "Daffodil"; and further off we can see the destroyers. Sir Roger Keyes on the "Warwick" signals from his mast head: "St. George for England!" The "Vindictive" answers: "May we give the dragon's tail a jolly good twist!" and runs alongside the Mole.

The dashing of the waves, the cries of the wounded, the roar of the artillery, the crashing explosions of the shells, which fall every second, make a din beyond the power of the mind to conceive. We stand on deck waiting for the scaling ladders to be placed against the Mole. A shell bursts and wipes out a gun crew; they are replaced by others, who in their turn are killed. Men fall faster and faster. Bullets and shell splinters fly like hail. It seems impossible to stand up and live. We see dark forms running towards the viaduct. The stormers are on the Mole. We climb a ladder and follow.

Now the marines advance, blowing up each shed as they come to it, and instantly disposing of the few Germans whom they find. Lieutenant Rigby on the conning tower of his ship is killed by a shell. Yet, in spite of the horrible confusion, the darkness, the noise and the danger, the wounded are passed back carefully and quickly to the "Vindictive." At the ladders are stationed men who help them down to the ship's deck and below, where they are at once examined by the surgeons.

Now the Mole is clear and we are at the commencement of the viaduct, which we observe to be crowded with the enemy, who are watching something on the seaward side. We peer into the gloom and discern a submarine moving along the surface of the water, steering straight for the viaduct. On her deck are mustered a little group of men, who bear charmed lives. The boat approaches the viaduct and runs between two piers, and there sticks fast. The crew hastily jump into the dinghy. An officer (Lieutenant Sandford) moves about igniting fuses, and then he also drops into the dinghy. The sailors push off and row out to sea as quickly as they can.

The Germans recover from their surprise, and a rattle of rifle fire commences. It is apparent that the little craft is hit again and again, and that several of her crew are wounded : moreover they are rowing against a strong current, and make but slow progress. When they are two or three hundred yards away, a blinding sheet of flame bursts from the submarine, and there is a report so mighty that it reduces even the deafening noise of the conflict to a seeming silence. A moment afterwards showers of *débris* fall all around us, on the Mole and on the water. The submarine has been blown to atoms and has completely wrecked a portion of the viaduct. . . .

G

The Submarine was blown to atoms (page 107).

The men in the submarine took their lives in their hands in order to make sure that she would reach a suitable spot, they disdained the offer of getting away earlier from the doomed vessel, they went to the extreme of human daring, and they successfully accomplished their work. They knew that, if their means of escape failed them, they would all be killed or drowned ; half of them were wounded, and their commander was wounded twice. Yet they went about their work as coolly as if they were practising manœuvres in peaceful waters.

About the time when the submarine exploded under the viaduct the third act in this night of marvels began to develop. The men on the Mole and the watching enemy on the viaduct turned their eyes eastwards. Three ships—the " Thetis," the " Intrepid," and the " Iphigenia "—were entering the harbour. Instantly their decks were swept by a storm of bullets. The " Thetis," which led the way, ran into nets which had been placed to guard the canal, and, as she had great holes in her sides where she had been hit by shells, she soon began to sink. The " Intrepid " followed, belching flame and smoke from every gun. She had better luck than her predecessor, for she was able to steer right into the mouth of the canal, where she was sunk in the middle of the channel, partly blocking the entrance. The " Iphigenia," which came last, collided with a dredger and a barge, pushed the barge before her into the canal, and was there blown up in such a position as to complete the work of closing the entrance. No submarine ever came again from Zeebrugge to attack our merchant ships.

Motor launches attended these three blockships, and took off the crews when they abandoned their vessels. It was supposed that there would be small hope of escaping alive, but the skill of the men in the launches was as great as their bravery, and few lives were lost in this part of the adventure.

The party on the Mole had now been away from their ships for an hour, and the work of destruction was finished. As the German fire from battery and machine gun was as devastating as ever, and no time was to be wasted before retiring, the "Daffodil" sounded the signal for retreat with her syren. At ten minutes past one, when every sailor had left the Mole, the "Vindictive," twisted, battered, and rent, but still seaworthy, was pulled away by her consorts.

Some indication of the dangers of the night may be gained from the fact that the "Iris," after she had started on her homeward journey, was hit by fifteen shells, her captain being killed, and she herself being set on fire.

Meanwhile the attack on Ostend had failed. The changing of the wind had altered the position of a buoy on which the assailants had relied for a knowledge of their position, with the result that, though the blocking ships had been sunk, they had not been sunk so as to close the canal.

To prevent a second attack the Germans cut gaps in the piers, stationed destroyers as a guard, and defaced the guide marks. Having done these things, they felt safe. But their very feeling of security was the source of their destruction, for Sir Roger Keyes determined to try again. The "Vindictive" was hastily repaired, Commander Godsal was put in charge of her, and a second attack was launched on the 9th of May.

The story of the end of this vessel is glorious and pathetic. When she came within sight of her task, with the shells from the monitors passing over, the smoke clouds were loosed and dense fog also came down, hiding her from the enemy and the enemy from her. Her partners, the "Brilliant" and the "Sirius," lost their way, but the "Vindictive" herself managed to steam right into the mouth of the canal. By this time she was dreadfully damaged. Commander Godsal and the officer who navigated her were both killed, and the conning tower had been demolished by a shell bursting upon it. In consequence, she was blown up by her engineer, after the crew had got away in the motor launches.

The deed was done! The canals were sealed! Victorious in death, the "Vindictive" lay sunk beneath the water, guarding the shores and homes of England as surely and as well as any vessel that still rides the waves, and to be remembered with the "Revenge" and her peers as long as the British Empire and the British Navy shall endure.

Exercises.

I.

1. Why did the expedition attack Zeebrugge?
2. What harm were the German submarines doing to British ships?
3. What are:—a submarine, a monitor, a viaduct, a mole, a dinghy, a blockship?
4. Who was the famous sailor who burnt the Spanish war vessels in Cadiz?
5. Who was the leader of the expedition against Zeebrugge?
6. Give the names of the principal ships.
7. How was the entrance to the canal at Zeebrugge defended?
8. Why was the attack so dangerous to make?
9. What were the three chief exploits?
10. What was the *Vindictive's* signal?
11. How were the crews of the blockships rescued?
12. Why did the first attack on Ostend fail?
13. What was the end of the *Vindictive*?

II.

[Use a dictionary to help you to answer this question.]

What is the meaning of?—departure, heroism, combatant, exhausted, gigantic, dogged, secure, maim, abominable, indignation, hostile, unmatched, volunteer, daunt, terminate, breakwater, hazardous, radiance, overwhelm, conflict, assailant.

III.

1. Tell the story of the *Vindictive* under the following headings.
   (1) The *Vindictive* starts on her journey.

(2) The arrival at Zeebrugge.
(3) The attack on the Mole.
(4) The return.
(5) The attack on Ostend.
(6) The sinking of the *Vindictive* in the canal.

2. Imagine yourself to be one of the men in the submarine which blew up the viaduct, and relate your adventures, in a letter written to a friend immediately after the event.

3. " Sir Richard Grenville, on the *Revenge,* delayed at the Azores Islands to take off some sick men, and was surrounded by a fleet of fifty-three Spanish ships of war. As he refused to surrender, the Spaniards attacked the *Revenge.* The cannon shots of the enemy could not touch the little *Revenge,* because their ships stood too high out of the water, while she was able to do great damage to them with her guns. When the Spaniards tried to board her, they were fiercely repulsed by the Englishmen. After twenty-four hours' fighting, when many of the crew had been killed, the survivors compelled Sir Richard to surrender. The next day he died of wounds, and shortly afterwards the *Revenge* sank during a storm."

Tell this story at greater length.

Ye Mariners of England.

Ye Mariners of England,
Who guard our native seas ;
Whose flag has braved, a thousand years,
The battle and the breeze !
Your glorious standard launch again
To match another foe !
And sweep through the deep,
While the stormy winds do blow ;
While the battle rages loud and long,
And the stormy winds do blow.

The spirits of your fathers
Shall start from every wave !
For the deck it was their field of fame,
And ocean was their grave :
Where Blake and mighty Nelson fell,
Your manly hearts shall glow,
As ye sweep through the deep,
While the stormy winds do blow ;
While the battle rages loud and long,
And the stormy winds do blow.

Britannia needs no bulwarks,
No towers along the steep ;

Her march is o'er the mountain-waves,
Her home is on the deep.
With thunders from her native oak
She quells the floods below,—
As they roar on the shore,
When the stormy winds do blow;
When the battle rages loud and long,
And the stormy winds do blow.

The meteor flag of England
Shall yet terrific burn;
Till danger's troubled night depart,
And the star of peace return.
Then, then, ye ocean-warriors!
Our song and feast shall flow
To the fame of your name,
When the storm has ceased to blow;
When the fiery fight is heard no more,
And the storm has ceased to blow.

T. Campbell.

A Brazilian Forest.

(Adapted from Bates' "A Naturalist on the Amazons.")

At its edge the lofty forest towered up like a wall to the height of probably one hundred feet. The tree trunks were only seen partially here and there, nearly the whole front from ground to summit being covered with a drapery of creeping plants, all of the most vivid shades of green ; scarcely a flower was to be seen, except in some places a solitary scarlet passion-flower, set in the green mantle like a star.

The low ground on the borders between the forest wall and the path was encumbered with a tangled mass of bushes and shrubs, amongst which prickly mimosas were very numerous, covering the other bushes in the same way as brambles do in England. Cassia trees, with their elegant foliage and showy yellow flowers, formed a great proportion of the lower trees, and anemones grew in groups around the swampy hollows.

Over the whole fluttered brilliantly-coloured butterflies, some wholly orange or yellow, others, with very long wings, sailing horizontally through the air, coloured black, and varied with blue, red, and yellow. One magnificent grassy-green species especially attracted our attention.

The sun was now exceedingly powerful. The day was most brilliant. The sky was without a cloud.

A Brazilian Forest.

We saw or heard no animals or birds. The very soil was hot to our feet, and we hastened into the shade of the forest.

On entering it, what a relief! We found ourselves in a moderately broad pathway or alley, where the branches of the trees crossed overhead and produced a delightful shade. The woods were dense and utterly impenetrable, and the ground, instead of being clothed with grass and shrubs, as in the woods of Europe, was everywhere carpeted with moss.

Gradually the scene changed. We descended slightly from an elevated, dry and sandy area to a low and swampy one; a cool air breathed upon our faces, and a mouldy smell of rotting vegetation greeted us. The trees were now taller, the under-wood less dense, and we could obtain glimpses into the wilderness on all sides. The leafy covers of the trees, scarcely two of which could be seen together of the same kind, were now far away above us—in another world, as it were. We could only see at times, where there was a break above, the tracery of the foliage against the clear, blue sky. Some-times the leaves were of the shape of large outstretched hands, at others, finely cut or feathery.

Below, the tree trunks were everywhere linked together by the woody, flexible stems of climbing and creeping trees. Some were twisted in strands like cables, others had thick stems contorted in every variety of shape, entwining snake-like round the tree trunks, or forming gigantic loops and coils

among the larger branches ; others, again, were
of zigzag shape, or indented like the steps of a stair-
case, sweeping from the ground to a giddy height.

Farther on the ground became more swampy,
and we had some difficulty in picking our way. The
wild banana here began to appear, and, as it grew
in masses, imparted a new aspect to the scene. The
leaves of this beautiful plant are like broad sword-
blades, eight feet in length and a foot broad ; they
rise straight upwards, alternately, from the top of
a stem five or six feet high. The trunks of the trees
were clothed with climbing ferns, Bamboos and
other tall grass and reed-like plants arched over
the pathway.

The appearance of this part of the forest was strange
in the extreme ; description can convey no adequate
idea of it. The reader who has visited Kew may
form some notion by conceiving plants like those
in the great palm-house at Kew Gardens spread
over a large tract of swampy ground, but he must
fancy it mingled with large trees covered with creepers
and figure to himself the ground encumbered with
fallen and rotting trunks, branches, and leaves ;
the whole illuminated by a flaming tropical sun, and
reeking with moisture.

In these tropical forests each plant and tree seems
to be striving to outdo its fellow, struggling upwards
towards light and air—branch and leaf and stem—
regardless of its neighbours. Climbing plants are
seen fastening with firm grip on others, making

use of them with reckless indifference as instruments for their own advancement.

There is one kind of tree which exhibits this feature in a very prominent manner. It is called the Sipo Matador or the Murderer Liana. The base of its stem would be unable to bear the weight of the upper growth : it is obliged therefore to support itself on a tree of another species. In this it is not different from other climbing trees and plants, but the way the Matador sets about it is peculiar, and disagreeable. It springs up close to the tree on which it intends to fix itself, and the wood of its stem grows by spreading itself over one side of the trunk of its supporter. It then puts forth, from each side, an armlike branch, which grows rapidly, and looks as though a stream of sap were flowing and hardening as it went. This adheres closely to the trunk of the victim, and the two arms meet on the opposite side and blend together. These arms are put forth at somewhat regular intervals in mounting upwards, and the victim, when its strangler is full-grown, becomes tightly clasped by a number of hard rings. The rings gradually grow larger as the Murderer flourishes, rearing its crown of foliage to the sky mingled with that of its neighbour, and in course of time they kill it by stopping the flow of its sap. The strange sight then remains of the selfish parasite clasping in its arms the lifeless and decaying body of its victim, which had been a help to its own growth. Then, when the dead trunk moulders away, its own end approaches; its support is gone, and itself also falls.

Farther on, what attracted us chiefly were the colossal trees. The general run of trees had not remarkably thick stems: the great and uniform height to which they grow without emitting a branch was much more noticeable than their thickness: but at intervals of a furlong or so a huge giant towered up.

Only one of these monstrous trees can grow within a given space: it occupies the domain, and none but individuals of much inferior size can find a footing near it. The trunks of these larger trees were generally about twenty or twenty-five feet round. Their total height, stem and crown together, may be estimated at from 180 to 200 feet: where one of them stands, the vast dome of foliage rises above the other forest trees as a domed cathedral does above the other buildings in a city.

Each day at dawn the sky was quite cloudless, and the heavy dew, or the previous night's rain, which lay on the moist foliage, was quickly dried by the glowing sun, which, rising straight out of the east, mounted rapidly towards the highest point in the sky. All nature was fresh, new leaf and flower buds expanding rapidly.

Some mornings a single tree would appear in flower amidst what was the preceding evening a green mass of forest—a dome of blossom suddenly created as if by magic. The birds were all active:

from the wild-fruit trees we often heard the shrill yelping of the toucans. Small flocks of parrots flew over on most mornings, at a great height, appearing in distinct relief against the blue sky, always two by two, chattering to each other, the pairs being separated by regular intervals.

The heat increased rapidly towards two o'clock, by which time every voice of bird or animal was hushed; only in the trees was heard at intervals the harsh whirr of a cicada. The leaves, which were so moist and fresh in early morning, now became lax and drooping; the flowers shed their petals.

On most days in June and July a heavy shower would fall some time in the afternoon, producing a most welcome coolness. The approach of the rain-clouds was after a fashion most interesting to observe. First, the cool sea-breeze, which commenced to blow about ten o'clock, and which had increased in force with the increasing power of the sun, would flag and finally die away. The heat of the atmosphere would then become insupportable. Languor and uneasiness would seize on everyone, even the denizens of the forest betraying it by their motions. White clouds would appear in the east, with an increasing blackness along their lower portions. The whole eastern horizon would become almost suddenly black, and then would spread upwards, the sun at length being darkened. Then the rush of a mighty wind is heard through the forest, swaying the tree-tops ; a vivid flash of lightning bursts forth, then a crash of thunder, and down streams the deluging rain.

Such storms soon cease, leaving bluish-black motionless clouds in the sky until night. Meantime all nature is refreshed ; but heaps of flower-petals and fallen leaves are seen under the trees.

Towards evening life revives again, and the ringing uproar is resumed from bush and tree. The following morning the sun again rises in a cloudless sky, and so the cycle is completed ; spring, summer, and autumn, as it were, in one tropical day. The days are more or less like this throughout the year, although a little difference exists between the wet and dry seasons.

There is a great variety of animals, birds, and reptiles in the Amazonian forests, but they are widely scattered and all very shy of man. The region is so large, and so uniform in its forest clothing, that it is only at long intervals that animals are seen in abundance, where some particular spot is found which is more attractive than others. There are monkeys, of course, but often we did not see or hear them, and no tapir or jaguar crossed our path. The sloth is rare, and even birds are scarce in many parts.

We often read, in books of travels, of the silence and gloom of the Brazilian forests. They are realities, and the impression deepens on a longer acquaintance. The few sounds of birds intensify the feeling

H

of solitude rather than imparting a sense of life and cheerfulness. Sometimes, in the midst of the stillness, a sudden yell or scream will startle one ; this comes from some defenceless fruit-eating animal, which is pounced upon by a tiger-cat or stealthy boaconstrictor.

Morning and evening, in most places, the howling monkeys make a fearful and harrowing noise, under which it is difficult to keep up one's lightness of spirit. The feeling of wildness which the forest inspires is increased tenfold under the fearful uproar.

Often, even in the still hours of midday, a sudden crash will be heard resounding afar through the wilderness, as some great bough or entire tree falls to the ground. There are, besides, many sounds which it is impossible to account for. Sometimes a sound is heard like the clang of an iron bar against a hard, hollow tree, or a piercing cry rends the air ; these are not repeated, and the succeeding silence tends to heighten the unpleasant impression they make on the mind. With the natives it is always the wild man or spirit of the forest which produces all noises which they are unable to explain.

Exercises.
I.
Complete the following sentences in a suitable manner :—

(a) The edge of the forest towered up like ——

(b) Flowering creepers covered the bushes as ——
(c) Brightly-coloured butterflies flew through the air like ——
(d) The trees were as tall as ——
(e) The palm leaves resembled ——
(f) The stems of the creepers twined round the tree-trunks like ——
(g) The crown of this great tree rose above the rest as ——
(h) Blossoms would suddenly appear as if ——
(i) The sky became as black as ——
(j) A crash re-echoed through the forest like ——

II.

1. Describe an oak, or an ash, or a willow.
2. Describe a Brazilian forest, employing the following headings :—

    (a) Heat.   (d) Flowers.
    (b) Trees.   (e) Climbing plants.
    (c) Birds.   (f) Animals.

3. Write a letter to a boy or girl in Brazil, describing some of the trees, flowers, animals, birds and insects found in the woods of Britain.

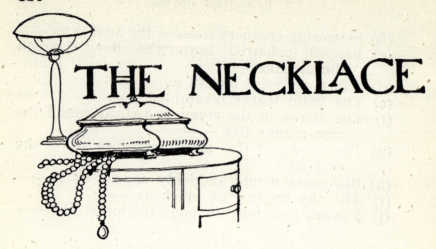

THE NECKLACE

(Abridged from Jean Ingelow's "The Suspicious Jackdaw.")

There was never a more suspicious creature in this world than Mrs. Mortimer, unless it was Mrs. Mortimer's jackdaw. To see him peep about, and turn his head on one side as if to listen, and go and stand on the edge of her desk with his bright eye fixed on her letters, and then flutter to her wardrobe, as if he suspected that, in cracks and crevices, under tables and behind screens, there must be other daws hidden, who would interfere with his particular interests, or listen to the remarks made to him when he and his mistress were alone, or find the bits of crust that he had stowed away for his own eating—to see all this, I say, was quite as good amusement as to see old Mrs. Mortimer occupying herself in the same way.

Sometimes Mrs. Mortimer would steal up softly

to her door, and turn the handle very softly in her hand ; then she would open it just a little, and listen till she must have had the earache ; but generally, after this exercise, she would return to her seat, saying aloud, as she took up her knitting : " Well, I declare, I thought that was the butcher's boy talking to Patience : an idle young fellow he is ; brings all the gossip of the village here, I 'm certain. However, this once I 'm wrong."

Here the jackdaw would give a little croak. Whenever his mistress finished a speech, he made a point of either croaking or coughing. His mistress could never help laughing when she heard him cough. No more could little Patience Grey, who was Mrs. Mortimer's maid. She was very young, only fourteen : but then Mrs. Mortimer suspected that if she had an older maid she would have more trouble keeping her in order.

So she took Patience from school to wait on her, and Patience was very happy, and, as there really seemed to be nothing about her for either Mrs. Mortimer's or the jackdaw's suspicion to rest upon, she was very seldom scolded, though sometimes when she came in looking rather hot and breathing quickly, her mistress would alarm her by saying : " Patience, you 've been skipping in the yard. You need not deny it, for I know you have ! "

Here Patience would answer, blushing : " I just skipped for a few minutes, ma'am, after I had done plaiting your frills."

"Ah, you'll never be a woman," Mrs. Mortimer would answer, "never! if you live to be a hundred."

And it did not enter into the head of little Patience that her mistress could see everything that was done in the yard, and how she sometimes ran and played with the house-dog under the two walnut-trees that grew there; and how she sometimes played at ball there when she had finished her work. It never entered her giddy head that her mistress could see all this; for her mistress sat in a large upper room, and, though one of its windows overlooked the yard, the blind was always drawn down. And how could Patience suppose that her mistress could peep through a tiny hole in it, and that she did this continually, so that the postman could not even politely offer her an orange without being seen by the keen eyes of Mrs. Mortimer?

Patience, however, fared none the worse for being watched—quite the contrary; the more the jackdaw and his mistress watched her, the fonder they grew. She was such a guileless little maid that they liked to have her with them. One day, when she was sent for to attend her mistress, she found her with the contents of an old cabinet spread open before her : there were corals with silver bells, there were old silver brooches, and there were many rings and old-fashioned ornaments that Patience thought extremely handsome. In particular, there was a red cornelian necklace which she considered to be particularly beautiful.

So did the jackdaw; for, when Mrs. Mortimer allowed Patience to wash the necklace in some warm water, he stood on the edge of the basin pecking at it playfully, as if he wanted to get it from her. Patience would not let him have it, and when she had carefully dried it, she laid it on some clean cotton wool, and said to the jackdaw : " You are not going to have it, Jack. It 's the most beautiful thing that Mistress has got, so I reckon she 'll never let you touch it."

When Mrs. Mortimer heard this, she smiled to think that Patience did not know the small value of cornelians. Just at this moment some visitors came, and Mrs. Mortimer retired to her own room previous to seeing them. She turned the key of the room where all her jewellery lay about, and the jackdaw, as he hopped with her out of the room, coughed approvingly at the deed, in a manner as expressive as if he said "Who knows whether all the people about us are honest?"

The old lady put the key into her basket; but, strange to say, she forgot her basket, leaving it in her bedroom when she went down to receive her visitors. And all that evening, suspicious as she was, she not once remembered that anyone could unlock the diningroom door by means of the key in the basket. On the contrary, she was in very good

The Jackdaw flew round the house in the moonlight.

spirits, and she and her visitors talked nearly all the evening about their servants, and about what a trouble servants were.

The visitors stayed late, and Patience went to bed in her little room at the top of the house. Not so Jack! When all was quiet, except in the parlour, he flew once or twice round the house in the clear moonlight, to see that other birds were asleep. Next he settled on the roof and walked cautiously to a certain crevice, where he kept some nails which he had pulled out of the carpets, together with bits of ribbons, and broken crockery. These he dragged out of the crevice, and poked with his beak, chattering all the while, and finally deposited them again in their hiding-place.

Then he flew down to a window, which was wide open at the top, and, entering, alighted on the table. There lay the cornelian necklace, looking very pretty. The jackdaw pecked at it for a bit, and lifted it up and shook it. At last he flew with it out of the window.

It was still quite light out of doors, and as the necklace dangled from his beak he admired it very much. He did not go to the roof, but alighted on the edge of a well in the garden, where he had previously placed his mistress's silver thimble, and a pair of scissors. He peered down into the well, and saw his own image, and the red necklace in his beak, and four or five stars reflected in the water. And, as it was his bed-time, he dozed as he stood on the edge of the well, and his beak opened owing

to the weight of the stones, and the necklace fell
into the water with a splash, where it sank at once

R. EADIE

to the bottom. Jack awoke with a start. But he
did not mind, for he was pleased with the sound
of splashing. He stood chattering to himself with
great serenity of mind for a time, and then went
to his bed.

This is what the jackdaw did. What did Mrs.
Mortimer do, when she walked to the parlour door
next morning, found the key in the basket, went
in, and saw that the necklace was gone?

She was quite amazed. Nobody but Patience
knew the necklace was there. Patience had admired

the necklace. Patience must have stolen the neck-lace,—little Patience, her good little maid, who seemed so guileless and honest. Oh, what a sad thing it was that there was nobody in the world that she could trust!

The old lady was so sorry to think of this that she decided to let Patience have a little time to reflect upon her great fault, and to confess. So she said nothing to her all the morning, and in the afternoon, peeping through her little hole in the blind, she saw Patience chasing the ducks into the pond, and laughing heartily to see them plunge. "Hardened girl," said her mistress, "how can she laugh?" and thereupon she sat down in her easy chair and began to cry. She had not supposed that she cared so much for this little maid of hers until she felt obliged to suspect her. She did not perceive how bad her own constant habit of suspicion was, and how it had obtained such dominion over her that she viewed everything in a false light.

This unhappy state of things went on for several days. At length Mrs. Mortimer happened to look out of the window and saw Patience cautiously looking down into her hand, which she was holding almost closed. She felt convinced that the poor child had the necklace concealed there. She drew up the blind, opened the window, and said, in an awful voice: "Patience, come here!" There was a verandah outside the window, and some wooden steps led up to it. Patience came up the steps, and her mistress sat down and looked at her through the open window. "Patience," said she, "I have lost my red necklace," and paused.

"Do you know where it is, Patience?" was the next question, asked with great solemnity. Patience tightened the folds of her apron, looked earnestly at her mistress, and said, "No, ma'am."

"Poor child," replied Mrs. Mortimer, shaking her head, and, Patience, appearing not to know what she meant, coloured exceedingly, and looked as if she was going to cry.

"Patience," said Mrs. Mortimer, "Show me what you have in your hand."

"Please, ma'am," replied Patience, opening her hand, "it's a glowworm that I found in the garden."

"Bless my soul," exclaimed Mrs. Mortimer, but she looked much less angry than before, and told Patience that she could go.

Next morning she sent again for Patience, and said to her: "Patience, I told you that I had lost my red necklace. I must have you to help me to look for it. But first tell me whether you know where it is."

"I know where I think it is, ma'am," Patience answered quite simply.

"Where?" asked her mistress. But she spoke and looked so severely that Patience hung her head and faltered, and at last it turned out that she merely thought it might be in the empty side of the tea-caddy, because the jackdaw often put things there.

While the little maid spoke she looked so bashful and confused that her mistress was confirmed in her bad opinion of her. But she allowed her to help in searching for the lost necklace, " For, after all," she thought, " I may be mistaken."

However, the necklace was not to be found ; and, though the jackdaw chattered and bustled about a great deal, and told over and over again, in the jackdaw's language, what he had done with it, no-body took the slightest notice of him.

At last Mrs. Mortimer sent for the little maid's mother, and, without finding fault, said to her that she did not require the services of Patience any longer ; and when the mother said : " I hope it is for no fault that you part with her, ma'am," she replied evasively: " Patience has her faults as other people have," and with that answer the mother was obliged to be satisfied.

When Patience was gone, her mistress felt very unhappy. She had felt a pleasure in her company, and now she was lonely again. The jackdaw, too, appeared to feel dull ; there was nobody to play with him and to carry him on her shoulder. He was dull, too, because he had lost that pretty neck-lace, and he often went to the edge of the well, and gabbled loudly there. But all his chatter and regret would not make the necklace float.

After a time, however, he found someone else to amuse him, for one of Mrs. Mortimer's sons and his little boy came to visit her, and the jackdaw delighted in teasing the little fellow, by pecking at his heels and stealing his pencils or any other small things that he had. The boy, for his part, was constantly teasing the bird, stroking his feathers the wrong way, snatching away his crusts, or otherwise plaguing him.

"I wish Patience was here to play with that child and keep him from teasing my Jack," said the old lady one day.

"Who is Patience?" asked her son.

Then Mrs. Mortimer told him the whole story. When she had finished, her son said: "Mother, I believe you will end in suspecting me! Why didn't you ascertain whether the girl was guilty or not before sending her away?"

"I feel certain she is guilty," answered his mother. "I will never trust any servant in future. But you don't know what a painful thing it is to have nobody in the house whom you can trust."

"Excuse me, mother," replied her son, "you mean nobody that you do trust."

At this point the jackdaw hopped in with a croak. He hopped to a private little cupboard that he kept under a turned-up edge of the carpet in a corner of the room, and, bringing out five or six mouldy bits of bread, he laid them in a row on the rug, and walked about with an air of reflection, as if he was saying to himself: "Whether people talk or not, I must attend to my business."

"I never saw such a queer creature!" exclaimed the son.

"Why, Jack, you miser," said his mistress, "one would think you were starved."

The jackdaw gabbled something which was no doubt meant to be rude, and then, hearing footsteps outside the door, he hastily snatched up a piece of his mouldy property and flew with it to the top of the cabinet. There he stood staring at the remainder, fluttering his wings and making a great outcry, for he did not dare to fly down for it, because his little tormentor had just rushed into the room.

"Father, father!" cried the boy.

"What is it, Tom?" asked his father.

"Do red currants ever grow under water?" asked Tom.

"No," said his father.

"But," continued the boy, "there is something growing in the well, just under the water, that looks like currants," and he made such a fuss that his grandmother and father consented to go with him to see what it was.

The weather during all the summer had been remarkably dry, and the well now contained very little water. As soon, therefore, as they reached the spot, they saw the object that had excited Tom's curiosity.

"That is much too big for a bunch of currants," said Mrs. Mortimer, peering down. "I shouldn't wonder if it was my cornelian necklace. Patience must have thrown it down there when she knew that I suspected her."

A ladder was fetched, and Mrs. Mortimer's son
descended into the well, and secured the glittering
object, which, as we know, was in truth the necklace. The jackdaw had accompanied the party, and
stood on the stones screaming and screeching, as
if he thought he was going to be robbed. As soon
as the old lady caught sight of the necklace, she
cried : " That 's my necklace, sure enough," and
she held out her hand for it. But the sight was too
much for the jackdaw. He suddenly flew up, and
gave the hand a fierce peck with his hard bill. Mrs.
Mortimer uttered a little cry, and dropped the necklace on the ground. The bird darted at it, and flew
with it up into a tree. There he rested a few minutes,
playing with the wet beads, and shaking them in
the sunlight. His mistress's entreaties could not
bring him down, and in a few minutes he flew off
again and settled on the roof of the house.

There, in less than ten minutes, he was found
with his ill-gotten gains spread out before him.
Everything was taken from him, and when Mrs.
Mortimer saw articles whose loss had caused her
to suspect nearly everyone about her of theft, she
was so vexed that she actually shed tears. " Mother,"
said her son, " it seems to me that you have trusted
the only creature about you that was utterly un-
worthy of trust. It is plain that Jack must have
thrown your necklace down the well."

The old lady was so disheartened that she could
not say a word. But such is the audacity and hardi-

hood of a jackdaw's nature that at teatime Jack
stalked into the room with a grave expression of
countenance, and hopped on to the tea-table as if
he had not a sin upon his soul.

"Patience shall come back again," thought the
old lady. So the mother of Patience was sent for.
But alas! she expressed herself much obliged to
Mrs. Mortimer, and said that her cousin in London,
hearing that the little maid was out of a place, had
sent for her to serve in her shop. "I am going to
send her some clothes next week," she added, "and I
shall tell her, ma'am, that you have not forgotten her."

Mrs. Mortimer was very disappointed, but there
was no help for it. When the woman had gone,
Mrs. Mortimer said to herself: "It is all the
fault of that thieving jackdaw. I must leave off
suspecting people, for it is a bad habit. I wish
I hadn't sent Patience away. But perhaps, if I had
been kinder to her than I was, she would have given
me cause to suspect her."

This last thought showed that Mrs. Mortimer had
still to fight against the bad habit. She was very
tired after her disappointment, and, settling herself
in her chair, she fell asleep. When she awoke, the
necklace was gone again. And perhaps it is a proof
that she really was somewhat improved that, though
she said, "I suspect, Jack, you know where that
necklace is," she took no steps to find out, but left
the glittering stones in the greedy bird's keeping.
Moreover, she put a patch upon the hole in the blind,

so that she could never peep through it any more. And she seldom thought of little Patience without a sigh.

Exercises.

I.

1. Who was Patience Grey?
2. How did Mrs. Mortimer discover everything that happened in the yard of her house?
3. What did Mrs. Mortimer do with the key of the parlour when she went to receive visitors?
4. How did the Jackdaw steal the necklace?
5. What did he do with it?
6. Why did he not put it in his hoard on the roof?
7. Why did Mrs. Mortimer suspect Patience of stealing the necklace?
8. Who discovered the necklace?
9. What did Mrs. Mortimer do when she found that she had wrongly suspected Patience?
10. Why did Patience not come back to live with Mrs. Mortimer?

II.

1. In these sentences replace each italicised phrase by a single word :—
   (a) William Wallace was a man of *great strength*.
   (b) *Many a time* Mrs. Mortimer had watched the Jackdaw.
   (c) Maxen saw rocks *of wondrous height*.
   (d) Here the river flows *with great rapidity*.
   (e) Two streets meet *at that place*.

2. In these sentences replace each italicized word by a suitable phrase :—
   (a) Harold fought *bravely*.
   (b) The mariners came to a *lonely* island.
   (c) The wretched prisoner was left *alone*.

(d)** Tall poplars stand *proudly* on the river banks.
(e) Bevis returned *sadly* through the meadows.

III.

1. If the Jackdaw could speak, what would be his version of this story?
2. Relate a tale that you know about some tame animal.
3. Read the following story, and then relate it in your own words :—

ANDROCLES AND THE LION.

(a) Once there lived in Africa a slave called Androcles who had a cruel master.
(b) He escaped into the desert and hid in a cave.
(c) A lion entered the cave. Instead of attacking him, it came up limping and moaning.
(d) Androcles found a large thorn in its paw, which was very greatly inflamed.
(e) Tremblingly he extracted the thorn, and bound up the paw.
(f) After this the lion and the man lived together, in woods and caves.
(g) After three years Androcles went back to the city.
(h) There he was recognised as a runaway slave, and condemned to be torn to pieces by wild beasts.
(i) On the day of his execution, a hungry lion was let loose upon him. But to the surprise of the multitude it fawned upon him and licked his hands and face.
(j) It was his own lion, which had been captured while following him to the town.
(k) When he told his story he and the lion were released.

The Valley of Avalon (page 148).

Ogier the Dane.

In the days of Charles the Great there was born to the King of Denmark a son, of whom a wonderful story is told. It is said that six fairies, more beautiful than the evening sky, came to his cradle, and smiled to him and kissed him. The first said to him : " Ogier, the whole world shall ring with your fame, and you shall never know what fear is." The second foretold that he would always find battles to fight against wrongdoers and oppressors. "You shall never be conquered," promised the third. The fourth and fifth gave him the gifts of courtesy and love.

The sixth, who was of stately mien, for she was Morgan le Fay, Queen of the Fairies, looked long and earnestly at him. At last she said : " Ogier, you shall never die : after you have lived a glorious life on earth, I will take you to the land of Faery, and there, in Avalon, you shall dwell with me for ever."

As soon as she had spoken, the wondrous light that surrounded the six began to pale, and they vanished, no man knew whither.

When Ogier was fourteen years old he was sent as a hostage to France, and kept as a prisoner at St. Omer, in Picardy, where he became betrothed to Belisande, the daughter of the governor of the castle. After he had spent several years in this place, and had grown to manhood, he was summoned

Ogier fought like a lion (page 145).

by Charles to join in a crusade against the Saracens. Before he went he married the fair Belisande.

The army marched on till they came to Rome, which was in the hands of the enemy. A host of Paynims came forth, and a dreadful battle began. Ogier fought like a lion, slaying so many of his foes that he raised a rampart of dead around him. Thrice he saved the life of the Emperor, and at length the Saracens were routed and put to flight.

After the fight the Emperor embraced him, and for his bravery made him a knight, and one of the paladins of France.

Next day, when the battle was joined again, Ogier rode into the fray mounted upon a great horse. When the Franks began to give ground he rallied them, doing such mighty deeds that they took as their battle cry " Ogier the Dane." He fought the Saracen General in single combat and defeated him, but was captured by treachery, and thrown, loaded with chains, into a foul and gloomy dungeon. From there he made his escape with the aid of Gloriande, Queen of the Saracens ; for had not a fairy promised at his birth that all women should love him ?

A fresh attempt was made by Charles and Ogier against the Paynim host. This time they were completely victorious, Rome was freed from her enemies, and the Franks returned to their own country.

When Ogier reached St. Omer he found to his grief that Belisande was dead, leaving him a son whom he

named Baldwin ; and also that, his father having
died in his absence, he was the King of Denmark.
He was beside himself at the loss of his wife, and
for a while he remained in France. But at length
he recovered from his sorrow, and departed to
Denmark, where he ruled well and wisely for five
years.

When he had settled the land he returned to Paris,
and did homage to the Emperor for his kingdom.
The Emperor welcomed him, and placed him in
the place of honour at his right hand ; for he was
proud to have so famous and mighty a champion
among his peers. Ogier was at this time stronger
than any mortal man, and he was so huge of stature
and so heavy that no horse except his own black
steed, Broiefort, could carry him.

He had with him his son Baldwin, who was the
favourite of the whole camp. One day Baldwin and
Charlot, the Emperor's son, were playing at chess.
During the game they began to quarrel, and Charlot,
who was the elder, struck Baldwin and killed him.
In consequence of this, Charles and Ogier had a
bitter quarrel, and Ogier returned to his own country,
where he raised an army, and made war upon the
Franks. With his magic sword Courtain, whose
edge was so sharp that no coat of mail, however
tough, could resist its stroke, he wrought great
damage. But at length he was a second time overcome by treachery and once more thrown into prison.

In time, however, a new war against the Sara-

cens forced Charles to release Ogier. Once more
the hero was mounted on Broiefort, and rode out
to battle. Wherever he went he was victorious.
He slew the giant Bruhier, and no castle could withstand his assault. But ever he thought of France,
the beautiful land which he had learnt to love, and
as soon as the war was over he took ship, hoping
there to end his days in peace, for he had grown
weary of endless war, and now he was a hundred
years old.

During the voyage a great storm arose, and battered
the vessel. Hither and thither it was tossed by
the wind, and the rudder and masts were broken.
Then a current carried it against a rock, where all
on board were drowned, saving Ogier alone. He

R. EADIE

stood on the deck gazing out upon the night, seeing
only the angry waves, and hearing nothing but the

roar of the breakers. Then he bared his head, and, thanking God for giving him his life, as a soldier should he quietly expected his end.

Darker grew the night, more terrible the storm. Ogier waited long, and his steadfast heart quailed not for a moment at the certain prospect of his death. But at length he heard a voice which called : " Ogier, Ogier, I wait for you. Fear nothing, but cast your-self upon the sea." And immediately he threw himself from the deck of the ship and was carried by a great billow upon a ledge of rock which ran along the bottom of the cliffs. There he found, by the aid of a strange light which dimly lit the gloom, a little path leading through the crags. He followed it till, wearied with his troubles and his labours, he lay down and slept.

When he awoke next morning he found himself in a delicious garden, where the trees stood fresh and green. It was the valley of Avalon. There everlasting spring abides, the flowers never fade, and no gathering storm ever spoils the azure sky. Ogier gazed round him in wonder, and while he did so he saw advancing across the lawns Morgan le Fay. Tall she was, and clad in shining white, and on her head was a golden crown.

She said to him : " Dear Knight, for a hundred years I have waited for you. Now that you have nobly spent on earth the span allotted to the sons of men, I have brought you here to me. Here you will live for ever, resting in peace." Then she placed upon his head the crown of forgetfulness, and he remembered his life on earth no more, and on his finger she put the ring of youth, so that the wrinkles of his face were smoothed away, his snow-white hair changed to gold, his limbs grew supple, and he was a young man once more.

On earth day followed day, spring became summer, summer was followed by autumn, which in its turn was succeeded by winter, year after year. Boys grew to be men and worked and fought. Charles the Great and all his peers died and were well nigh forgotten, so that the memory of Ogier dwindled into a tale. Fierce pirates came from the north and conquered Normandy, and oppressed the Franks, and no one could withstand them.

At length, Morgan le Fay, to whom all these things were known, in pity for the sufferings of men lifted the crown from Ogier's brows, and memory came back to him. He thought of Charles, and Baldwin and Belisande, and, standing up, asked for his sword. With tears in her eyes, Morgan le Fay brought it to him, and bade him go to fight for the fair land of France, as he had done in ancient days. He promised not to forget her and to return when he had driven the heathen away. Then, mounting his horse, he rode off.

When Ogier reached Paris the people flocked out to see this knight, so tall of stature and so handsome, who yet wore armour of a fashion so ancient that even the oldest men could not remember its like.

For what to Ogier had been but a single day of varied
and ceaseless delight had in reality been two hundred
years. When he told them that he was Ogier the
Dane, they laughed and thought he was mad. But

R. EADIE

Morgan le Fay lifted the crown from Ogier's brows (page 149).

so strong did he look, and so fierce and grim was
his face, that they dared not jeer at him. Moreover,
he said that he had come to fight for them and for
France, and they were in sore distress and danger.

Next day Ogier rode out to meet the foe, who were already approaching the gates of Paris, driving the French before them. Just as in days of old he had fought the Saracens, Ogier, mounted on his great horse, spurred into the fight, and wherever he rode left behind him heaps of slain. And he cried in a great voice his battle cry: " Ogier, Ogier the Dane." When the soldiers heard it they turned and followed him, and routed the assailants, and put them to flight. Soon the land was cleared of the invaders, and Ogier returned to the Court. He told his story, but ever he kept upon his finger the ring which preserved his youth.

One day, as he lay asleep beside a fountain in the garden of the palace, the Queen happened to pass by with one of her maids, the lady of Senlis. The latter, remembering Ogier's strange story, and, seeing upon his hand the ring, which was ornamented with strange jewels, determined to test the truth of the legend. Quietly she slipped the ring from his finger, and put it on her own. No sooner had she done so than Ogier changed. His mighty limbs became thin and weak, his face creased into wrinkles, his sunny locks grew white. He awoke uneasily and opened his eyes, an old man, on whom the toils of three hundred winters had left their mark.

Seeing the ring in the countess's hand, he stretched out a shaking and withered arm, and in a cracked, quavering voice asked for it. She was unwilling to restore it, but the Queen was horror-struck at the pitiful sight, and forced her maid to replace it upon Ogier's finger. Immediately his youth was restored, so that they could scarcely believe that any change had occurred. Then did they know that he was in truth, as he had always said, Ogier the Dane.

Shortly afterwards the King of France died, and his young Queen, remembering the deeds and fame of Ogier, thought that she could not do better than marry him. Ogier had forgotten Morgan le Fay, and he felt that to sit on the throne of his master, Charles, was the greatest honour that he could receive. The people rejoiced greatly when they heard that their champion was to be their king, for they knew

R. EADIE.

Hand in hand, they went out, and toward the rising sun (page 153).

that they would be safe from all attack while he ruled over them. Great preparations were made for the ceremony, the churches were decorated, and in every street banners were displayed.

But it was not to be. On the morning of the wedding, before daybreak, Ogier was awakened by a voice which called as it had called once before: " Ogier, Ogier, I wait for you." A bright light shone, and Morgan le Fay approached, with outstretched arms. As soon as Ogier saw her, remembrance came back to him, and he arose, and went to her. Then, hand in hand, they went out, and toward the rising sun, and no one has ever beheld them since.

But still men say that Ogier sleeps in Avalon till the day when France shall be in danger. When that day comes he will return to earth, to fight again for the land he guarded and loved so well, and when he comes, the Franks will turn and conquer their foes, rallying to the battle-cry which in days of yore brought them victory, the cry of " Ogier! Ogier the Dane! "

Exercises.

1. What were the gifts that the fairies promised to Ogier at his birth?
2. Where was Ogier imprisoned when he went to France?
3. How was Ogier rescued when all his companions were drowned
4. Who met him when he awoke on the morning after the shipwreck?

Ogier the Dane.

5. Where was he when he awoke ?
6. What gifts did Morgan le Fay give him ?
7. Why did Ogier go back to France again ?
8. How did the lady of Senlis discover Ogier's secret ?
9. Why did Ogier not marry the Queen of France, when the wedding had been arranged ?

II.

What is the meaning of :—hostage, Paynim, combat, rampart, vanish, treachery, victorious, dwindle, homage, azure, stature, steadfast, assailant, ceremony ?

[Use a Dictionary to help you in answering this question.]

III.

Relate one of the following tales :—
   (a) The Story of Oisin.   (b) Beowulf and Grendel.
   (c) Perseus and Andromeda.   (d) Joan of Arc.
   (e) Sir Patrick Spens.

Thomas the Rhymer.

True Thomas lay on Huntly bank ;
A ferlie[1] he spied wi' his e'e ;
And there he saw a lady bright
Come riding down by the Eildon-tree.

(1) marvel.

Her skirt was o' the grass-green silk
Her mantle o' the velvet fine ;
At ilka tett[2] o' her horse's mane
Hung fifty siller[3] bells and nine.

(2) lock.   (3) silver.

True Thomas he pulled aff his cap,
And louted[4] low down to his knee;
"All hail, thou mighty Queen of heaven!
For thy peer on earth I never did see."

(4) bowed.

"O no, O no, Thomas," she said,
"That name does not belong to me;
I am but the Queen of fair Elfland,
That hither am come to visit thee."

"Harp and carp[5], Thomas," she said,
"Harp and carp along wi' me;
And if ye dare to kiss my lips,
Sure of your body I will be."

(5) sing.

"Betide me weal, betide me woe,
That weird[6] shall never daunton[7] me;"
Syne[8] he has kissed her rosy lips,
All underneath the Eildon-tree.

(6) fate.   (7) frighten.   (8) at once.

"Now ye maun[9] go wi' me," she said;
"Now, Thomas, ye maun go wi' me;
And ye maun serve me seven years
Through weal or woe as may chance to be."

(9) must.

She 's mounted on her milk-white steed;
She 's ta'en True Thomas up behind :
And ay, whene'er her bridle rang,
The steed flew swifter than the wind.

O, they rode on, and farther on,
The steed gaed[10] swifter than the wind ;
Until they reached a desert wide,
And living land was left behind.

(10) went.

"Light down, light down now, True Thomas,
And lean your head upon my knee ;
Abide and rest a little space,
And I will show you ferlies three.

"O see ye not yon narrow road
So thick beset wi' thorns and briars ?
That is the Path of Righteousness,
Though after it but few enquires.

"And see ye not that braid[11], braid road,
That lies across the lily leven[12] ?
That is the Path of wickedness,
Though some call it the road to Heaven.

(11) broad.   (12) flowery meadow.

" And see ye not that bonny road,
That winds aboot the ferny brae[13] ?
That is the road to fair Elfland
Where thou and I this night maun gae.

(13) brow.

" But, Thomas, ye shall haud your tongue,
Whatever ye may hear or see ;
For, speak ye word in Elfin-land,
Ye 'll ne'er get back to your ain countree."

O they rode on, and farther on,
And they waded through rivers aboon the knee,
And they saw neither sun nor moon,
But they heard the roaring of the sea.

He has gotten a coat of the even cloth,
And a pair of shoes of velvet green ;
And till seven years were gane and past,
True Thomas on earth was never seen.

Exercises.

I.

Which verse of this poem do you like best ?　Give
reasons for your choice.

II.

1. Tell the story contained in " True Thomas " in
your own words.
2. Relate the story of Ogier the Dane.

к

The Archery Contest.

Persons :

Prince John.
Waldemar.
Locksley (Robin Hood disguised as a yeoman).
Hubert (an archer).

Waldemar.—The day is not yet very far spent. Let the archers shoot a few rounds at the target, and the prize be adjudged. The yeomen and commoners, now that the tournament is over, must not be dismissed discontented for lack of their share in the sports.

Prince John.—I thank thee, Waldemar. Thou remindest me, too, that I have a debt to pay to an insolent peasant that yesterday insulted our person, in applauding a Saxon who defied me. Fetch that yeoman hither. Were this my last hour of power, it should be an hour sacred to revenge and to pleasure. Let it be proclaimed that to the best archer a prize shall be awarded, being a bugle-horn mounted with silver, and a silken baldric richly ornamented with a medallion of the patron of silvan sport. [*The proclamation is made, and ten archers present themselves to shoot for the prize.*]

Waldemar.—We have the archer here, as your Highness commanded that he was on no account to be allowed to escape.

[Locksley steps forward.]

Prince John.—Fellow, I guessed by thy insolent babble thou wast no true lover of the long-bow when thou saidst thou didst ever love to see a good shot or a gallant blow. And I see thou darest not adventure thy skill among such merry men as stand yonder.

Locksley.—Under favour, sir, I have another reason for refraining to shoot, beside fearing discomfiture and disgrace.

Prince John.—And what is thy other reason?

Locksley.—Because I know not if these yeomen and I are used to shoot at the same marks ; and because, moreover, I know not how your grace might relish the winning of a prize by one who has unwittingly fallen under your displeasure.

Prince John.—What is thy name, yeoman?

Locksley.—My name is Locksley.

Prince John.—Then, Locksley, thou shalt shoot in thy turn, when these yeomen have displayed their skill. If thou carriest the prize, I will add to it twenty nobles ; but, if thou losest it, thou shalt be stript of thy Lincoln green, and scourged out of the lists with bowstrings, for a wordy and insolent braggart.

Locksley—And how if I refuse to shoot on such a wager ? Your Grace's power, supported, as it is, by so many men-at-arms, may indeed easily strip and scourge me, but cannot compel me to bend or to draw my bow.

Prince John.—If thou refusest my fair proffer, the Provost of the lists shall cut thy bowstring, break thy bow and arrows, and expel thee from the presence as a faint-hearted craven.

Locksley.—This is no fair chance you put on me, proud Prince, to compel me to peril myself against the best archers of Leicester and Stafford-shire, under the penalty of infamy if they should overshoot me. Nevertheless, I will obey your pleasure.

Prince John.—Look to him close, men-at-arms; his heart is sinking; I am jealous lest he attempt to escape the trial. [*To the archers who are to shoot*]: And do you, good fellows, shoot boldly round; a buck and a butt of wine are ready for your refreshment in yonder tent, when the prize is won.

[*The archers shoot one by one, and a forester named Hubert is victorious.*]

Prince John.—Now, Locksley, wilt thou try conclusions with Hubert, or wilt thou yield up bow, baldric, and quiver, to the Provost of the sports?

Locksley.—Sith it be no better, I am content to try my fortune; on condition that when I have shot two shafts at yonder mark of Hubert's, he shall be bound to shoot one at that which I shall propose.

Prince John.—That is but fair, and it shall not be refused thee.—If thou dost beat this braggart,

Hubert, I will fill the bugle with silver pennies
for thee.

Hubert.—A man can but do his best; but my
grandsire drew a good long-bow at Hastings, and
I trust not to dishonour his memory.

[*A fresh target is placed. Hubert shoots carefully. The arrow whistles through the air, and
lights within the inner ring of the target, but not
exactly in the centre.*]

Locksley.—You have not allowed for the wind,
Hubert, or that had been a better shot.

[*Locksley shoots carelessly. The arrow alights on
the target two inches nearer to the white spot in
the centre than that of Hubert.*]

Prince John (to Hubert).—By the light of Heaven,
an thou suffer that runagate knave to overcome
thee, thou art worthy of the gallows.

Hubert.—An your highness were to hang me,
a man can but do his best. Nevertheless, my grandsire drew a good bow——

Prince John.—A plague on thy grandsire and
all his generation. Shoot, knave, and shoot thy
best, or it shall be worse for thee.

[*Hubert shoots, allowing for the wind, and the
arrow hits the very centre of the target.*]

Prince John (with a smile of triumph).—Thou
canst not mend that shot, Locksley.

Locksley (to himself).—I will notch his shaft
for him, however.

[*He shoots with a little more care than before, and the arrow lights upon Hubert's, splitting it to shivers*.]

Prince John.—This must be the devil, and no man of flesh and blood.

Hubert.—Such archery was never seen since a bow was bent in Britain.

Locksley.—And now I will crave your Grace's permission to plant such a mark as is used in the North Country; and welcome to every yeoman who shall try a shot at it. Let your guards attend me, if you please. I go but to cut a rod from the next willow-bush. [*He leaves the lists and returns with a willow wand about six feet in length, and rather thicker than a man's thumb*.] To ask a good woodsman to shoot at a target so broad as that we have used is to put shame upon his skill. In the land where I was bred, men would as soon take for their mark King Arthur's Round Table, which held sixty knights round it. A child of seven years old might hit that target with a headless shaft. [*He walks to the end of the lists and sticks the willow wand upright in the ground*.] But he that hits that rod at five-score yards, I call him an archer fit to bear both bow and quiver before a king, an it were the stout King Richard himself.

Hubert.—My grandsire drew a good bow at the battle of Hastings, and never shot at such a mark in his life—and neither will I. If this yeoman can cleave that rod, I give him the bucklers, or rather

ROBT. EADIE

Locksley shot with great care (page 164).

I yield to the devil that is in his jerkin, and not to any human skill ; a man can but do his best, and I will not shoot where I am sure to miss. I might as well shoot at a wheat-straw, or at a sunbeam, as at a twinkling white streak which I can hardly see.

Prince John.—Cowardly dog ! Sirrah Locksley, do thou shoot ; but if thou hittest such a mark, I will say thou are the first man ever did so. Howe'er it be, thou shalt not crow over us with a mere show of superior skill.

Locksley.—I will do my best ; as Hubert says, no man can do more. [*He shoots with great care, the crowd waiting the result in breathless silence. His arrow splits the willow rod against which it was aimed. Shouts of applause arise on every side from the onlookers.*]

Prince John.—These twenty nobles, which, with the bugle, thou hast fairly won, are thine own ; we will make them fifty if thou wilt take livery and service with us as a yeoman of our body-guard, and be near to our person. For never did so strong a hand bend a bow, or so true an eye direct a shaft.

Locksley.—Pardon me, noble Prince, but I have vowed that, if ever I take service, it should be with your royal brother King Richard. These twenty nobles I leave to Hubert, who has this day drawn as brave a bow as his grandsire did at Hastings. Had his modesty not refused the trial he would have hit the wand as well as I. [*He bows and withdraws.*]

(Adapted from Sir Walter Scott's " Ivanhoe.")

Exercises.

I.

1. Who was Locksley?
2. Why was Prince John angry with him?
3. How did the Prince propose to punish Locksley?
4. Who was Hubert?
5. On what condition did Locksley agree to shoot?
6. What was the prize of the archery contest?
7. What was the mark which Locksley set up instead of the target?
8. Why did Locksley refuse to take service with Prince John?

II.

Join the following sentences, where you think they should be joined, by suitable words, so as to make a well-told story:—

An African was once driving a herd of cattle to a pool. They were going to drink. The pool was fenced in by steep walls of rock. The summer had been very hot. Water was scarce. The pool was lower than usual. The herd came close to the brink. Then the man noticed a huge lion. The lion was lying right in the water. It was preparing to spring. The African ran away as fast as he could. He ran through the herd. A low roar told him that the lion was chasing him. The lion did not attack any of the oxen. The man reached a tree. Just then the lion bounded into the air. The native threw himself upon his face. He was terrified. The lion missed him. The African climbed up the tree. He climbed up as fast as he could. The lion waited all night. In the morning he went away.

III.

Imagine yourself to be Robin Hood, and tell the story of the archery contest to one of your friends.

Elegy on the Death of a Mad Dog.

Good people, all of every sort,
Give ear unto my song ;
And if you find it wondrous short—
It cannot hold you long.

In Islington there dwelt a man
Of whom the world might say
That still a godly race he ran—
Whene'er he went to pray.

A kind and gentle heart he had,
To comfort friends and foes ;
The naked every day he clad—
When he put on his clothes.

And in that town a dog was found,
As many dogs there be,
Both mongrel puppy, whelp, and hound,
And curs of low degree.

This dog and man at first were friends ;
But, when a pique began,
The dog, to gain some private ends,
Went mad, and bit the man.

Around from all the neighbouring streets,
The wondering neighbours ran,
And swore the dog had lost his wits,
To bite so good a man.

The wound it seemed both sore and sad
To every Christian eye ;
And while they swore the dog was mad,
They swore the man would die.

But soon a wonder came to light
That showed the rogues they lied ;
The man recovered of the bite,
The dog it was that died.

Oliver Goldsmith.

One Eye.

Adapted from "White Fang," by Jack London.

[By kind permission of Mrs. Jack London and the publishers,
Messrs. Methuen & Co., Ltd.]

One Eye was hungry. Though he lay down in the entrance of the cave and slept, his sleep was fitful. He kept waking and cocking his ears at the bright world without, where the April sun was blazing across the snow. When he dozed, upon his ears would steal the faint whispers of hidden trickles of running water, and he would rise and listen intently. The sun had come back, and all the awakening northland world was calling to him. The feel of Spring was in the air, the feel of growing life under

the snow, of sap ascending in the trees, of buds bursting the shackles of the frost.

He cast anxious glances at his mate, but she showed
no desire to get up. He looked outside, and half-a-
dozen snow-birds fluttered across his field of vision.
He started to get up, then looked back to his mate
again, and settled down and dozed. A shrill and
minute singing stole upon his hearing. Once, and
twice, he sleepily brushed his nose with his paw.
Then he woke up. There, buzzing in the air at the
tip of his nose, was a lone mosquito. It was a full-
grown mosquito, one that had lain frozen in a dry
log all winter, and that had now been thawed out
by the sun. He could resist the call of the world
no longer. Besides, he was hungry.

He crawled over to the she-wolf and tried to persuade her to get up. But she only snarled at him,
and he walked out alone into the bright sunshine
to find the snow-surface soft under foot, and the
travelling difficult. He went up the frozen bed of
the stream, where the snow, shaded by the trees,
was yet hard and crystalline. He was gone eight
hours, and he came back through the darkness
hungrier than when he started. He had found game,
but he had not caught it. He had broken through
the melting snow-crust, while the snowshoe rabbits
had skimmed along on top lightly as ever.

At the mouth of the cave he paused with a sudden
shock of suspicion. Faint, strange sounds came
from within. They were sounds not made by his

mate, and yet they were remotely familiar. He crawled cautiously inside, and was met by a warning snarl from the she-wolf. This he received without dismay, though he obeyed it by keeping his distance ; but he remained interested in the other sounds— faint, muffled sobbings and mutterings.

His mate warned him crossly away, and he curled up and slept in the entrance. When morning came and a faint light shone through the lair, he again sought after the source of the strange sounds. There was a new note in his mate's warning snarl. It was a jealous note, and he was very careful in keeping a respectful distance. Nevertheless, he made out five little bundles of life, very feeble, very helpless, making tiny whimpering noises, with eyes that did not open to the light. He was surprised.

His mate looked at him anxiously. Every little while she uttered a low growl, and, at times, when it seemed to her he approached too near, the growl shut up in her throat to a sharp snarl. In her mind there lurked a memory of wolves that had eaten their new-born and helpless offspring.

But there was no danger. One Eye was feeling an impulse, and he obeyed it by trotting out and away on the meat-trail whereby he lived.

Five or six miles from the lair, the stream divided, its forks going off among the mountains at a right angle. Here, leading up the right fork, he came upon a fresh track. He smelled it, and found it so recent that he crouched swiftly and looked in the

direction in which it disappeared. Then he turned
and took the right fork. The footprint was much
larger than the one his own feet made, and he knew
that in the wake of such a trail there was little meat
for him.

Half-a-mile up the right fork, his quick ears caught
the sound of gnawing teeth. He stalked the quarry
and found it to be a porcupine, standing upright
against a tree and trying its teeth on the bark. One
Eye approached carefully but hopelessly. He knew
the breed, though he had never met it so far north
before ; and never in his long life had porcupine
served him for a meal. But he had long since learned
that there was such a thing as chance, and he continued to draw near. There was never any telling
what might happen, for with live things events were
somehow always happening differently.

The porcupine rolled itself into a ball of long, sharp
needles that defied attack. In his youth One Eye
had once sniffed too near a similar ball of quills,
and the tail had flicked out suddenly in his face.
One quill he had carried away in his muzzle, where
it remained for weeks, a rankling flame, until it
finally worked out. So he lay down, in a comfortable
crouching position, his nose fully a foot away, and
out of the line of the tail. Thus he waited, keeping
perfectly quiet. There was no telling. Something
might happen. The porcupine might unroll. There
might be opportunity for a deft and ripping thrust
of a paw into the tender, unguarded belly.

"He walked out alone into the bright sunshine" (page 168).

At the end of half-an-hour he arose, growled wrath-
fully at the motionless ball, and trotted on. He had
waited too long and uselessly in the past for porcu-
pines to unroll, to waste any more time. He continued
up the right fork. The day wore along, and nothing
rewarded his hunt.

In the afternoon he blundered upon a ptarmigan.
He came out of a thicket and found himself face to
face with the slow-witted bird. It was sitting on
a log, not a foot beyond the end of his nose. Each
saw the other. The bird made a startled rise, but
he struck it with his paw, smashed it down to the
earth, pounced upon it, and caught it in his teeth
as it scuttled across the snow trying to rise in the
air again. As his teeth crunched through the tender
flesh and fragile bones, he began naturally to eat.
Then he remembered, and, turning on the back-track,
started for home, carrying the ptarmigan in his mouth.

A mile above the forks, running velvet-footed as
was his custom, a gliding shadow that cautiously
looked along each new vista of the trail, he came
upon later imprints of the large tracks he had discovered in the early morning. As the track led his
way, he followed, prepared to meet the maker of
it at every turn of the stream.

He slid his head around a corner of rock, where
began an unusually large bend in the stream, and
his quick eyes made out something that sent him
crouching swiftly down. It was the maker of the
track, a large female lynx. She was crouching

as he had crouched once that day, in front of her the tight-rolled ball of quills. If he had been a gliding shadow before, he now became the ghost of such a shadow, as he crept and circled round, and came up well to leeward of the silent, motionless pair.

He lay down in the snow, depositing the ptarmigan beside him, and with eyes peering through the needles of a low-growing spruce he watched the play of life before him—the waiting lynx and the waiting porcupine, each intent on life ; and, such was the curiousness of the game, the way of life for one lay in the eating of the other, and the way of life for the other lay in not being eaten ; while old One Eye, the wolf, crouching in the covert, played his part, too, in the game, waiting for some strange freak of chance, that might help him on the meat-trail which was his way of life.

Half-an-hour passed, an hour ; and nothing happened. The ball of quills might have been a stone for all it moved ; the lynx might have been frozen to marble ; and old One Eye might have been dead.

At length One Eye moved slightly and peered forth with increased eagerness. Something was happening. The porcupine had at last decided that its enemy had gone away. Slowly, cautiously, it was unrolling its ball of armour. Slowly, slowly, the bristling ball straightened out and lengthened. One Eye, watching, felt a sudden moistness in his mouth, excited by the living meat that was spreading itself like a repast before him.

L

Not quite entirely had the porcupine unrolled when it discovered its enemy. In that instant the lynx struck. The blow was like a flash of light. The paw, with rigid claws curving like talons, shot under the tender belly and came back with a swift ripping movement. Had the porcupine been entirely unrolled, or had it not discovered its enemy a fraction of a second before the blow was struck, the paw would have escaped unscathed; but a side-flick of the tail sank sharp quills into it as it was withdrawn.

Everything had happened at once—the blow, the counter-blow, the squeal of agony from the porcupine, the big cat's squall of sudden hurt and astonishment. One Eye half arose in his excitement, his ears up, his tail straight out and quivering behind him. The lynx's bad temper got the best of her. She sprang savagely at the thing that had hurt her. But the porcupine, squealing and grunting, with torn body trying feebly to roll up into its ball-protection, flicked out its tail again, and again the big cat squalled with hurt and astonishment. Then she fell to backing away and sneezing, her nose bristling with quills like a monstrous pin-cushion. She brushed her nose with her paws, trying to dislodge the fiery darts, thrust it into the snow, and rubbed it against twigs and branches, and all the time leaping about, ahead, sidewise, up and down, in a frenzy of pain and fright.

She sneezed continually, and her stub of a tail was doing its best toward lashing about by giving quick, violent jerks. She quitted her antics, and quieted down for a long minute. One Eye watched, and even he could not repress a start when she suddenly leaped, without warning, straight into the air, at the same time emitting a long and most terrible squall. Then she sprang away, up the trail, squalling with every leap she made.

It was not until her racket had faded away in the distance, and died out, that One Eye ventured forth. He walked as carefully as though all the snow were carpeted with porcupine quills, erect and ready to pierce the soft pads of his feet. The porcupine met his approach with a furious squealing and a clashing of its long teeth. It had managed to roll up in a ball again, but it was not quite the old compact ball ; its muscles were too much torn for that. It had been ripped almost in half, and was still bleeding profusely.

One Eye scooped out mouthfuls of the blood-soaked snow, and chewed, and tasted, and swallowed. This served as a relish, and his hunger increased mightily : but he was too old in the world to forget his caution. He waited. He lay down and waited, while the porcupine grated its teeth and uttered grunts and sobs, and occasional little sharp squeals. In a little while, One Eye noticed that the quills were drooping, and that a great quivering had set up. The quivering came to an end suddenly. There was a final defiant clash of the long teeth. Then all the quills drooped quite down, and the body relaxed and moved no more.

With a nervous, shrinking paw, One Eye stretched out the porcupine to its full length, and turned it over on its back. Nothing had happened. It was surely dead. He studied it for a moment, then took a careful grip with his teeth, and started off down the stream, partly carrying, partly dragging the porcupine, with head turned to the side so as to avoid stepping on the prickly mass. He recollected something, dropped the burden, and trotted back to where he had left the ptarmigan. He did not hesitate a moment. He knew clearly what was to be done, and this he did by promptly eating the ptarmigan. Then he returned and took up his burden.

When he dragged the result of his day's hunt into the cave, the she-wolf inspected it, turned her muzzle to him, and lightly licked him on the neck. But the next instant she was warning him away from the cubs with a snarl that was less harsh than usual. He was behaving as a wolf-father should.

Exercises.

I.

1. Make a list of the animals and birds which are mentioned in this tale, and write a short description of one of them.
2. Why did not the wolf try to kill the porcupine?
3. Why did the wolf carry food to the cave instead of eating it himself?
4. Why did the wolf leave the track which he was following at first?

II.

Join the following pairs of sentences together by means of proper words :—

Model : Q.—Maggie looked through the bars of the gate into a field. The field was full of buttercups.

A.—Maggie looked through the bars of the gate into a field which was full of buttercups.

1. Maggie crept through the bars of the gate. Maggie walked on.
2. Fred was very brave. Unfortunately, he was very small.
3. The night has come. At night the birds and beasts go to rest.
4. Return this book to the library. It belongs to the library.

III.

1. Retell the story of One Eye, using the following headings :—
   (a) The wolf sets out in search of food.
   (b) He finds a porcupine.
   (c) He kills a ptarmigan.
   (d) The porcupine is killed by a lynx.
   (e) The wolf carries the porcupine to his mate.
2. Relate any other story that you know about wolves.
3. Retell this story, making One Eye tell it to another wolf.
4. Make a dialogue between the wolf and the she-wolf, using the following headings :—
   (1) The wolf is anxious to examine the cubs and is prevented by the she-wolf.
   (2) He goes out hunting.
   (3) He returns with a dead porcupine for the she-wolf.

The Death of Harold (page 184)

The Battle of Hastings

(Adapted from Creasy's "Fifteen Decisive Battles of the World.")

During the reign of Edward the Confessor, William, Duke of Normandy, laid claim to the crown of England. Little was thought of this at the time, but when Harold, the son of Earl Godwin, who had been chosen by the English as the successor of Edward, was in France, he fell into the power of the Duke. William made good use of his opportunity, and compelled Harold to promise that he would give his assistance to his rival.

On Edward's death, as Harold would not grant his claim, William invaded England with an army of sixty thousand men. The King was away in the

North at the time, and so the Normans were able to land without opposition.

Harold instantly hurried southwards to meet the long-expected enemy. He found the Normans encamped near the south coast at Hastings, in the county of Sussex. The Duke had fortified a camp there, and had set up two wooden castles which he had brought with him from Normandy in pieces all ready for framing together. The English had fled before him, driving off their cattle and quitting their houses.

When the English king was about seven miles from the Norman lines he halted and sent some spies to examine the number and preparations of the enemy, who, on their return, related with astonishment that there were more priests in William's camp than there were fighting men in the English army. They had mistaken the Norman soldiers, who cut their hair and shaved their chins, for priests. Harold, who knew the Norman usages, smiled at their words, and said : " Those whom you have seen in such numbers are not priests, but stout soldiers, as they will soon make us feel."

A neck of hills bends inwards from the high ground immediately to the north-east of Hastings, and along the summits of these lay, in ancient times, the route to London. At the distance of seven miles from Hastings, a valley must be crossed, opposite to which rises a high ground of some extent, facing the south-east. The high ground, then called Senlac, was occupied by Harold's army. It could not be attacked in front without considerable disadvantage to the assailants, and could hardly be passed without those engaged in the movement exposing themselves to a fatal charge in the flank, while they wound round the base of the height. There was a rough and thickly-wooded district in the rear, which seemed to offer Harold great facilities for rallying his men, and checking the progress of the enemy, if they should succeed in forcing him back from his post. And it seemed scarcely possible that the Normans, if they met with any repulse, could save themselves from utter destruction.

With such hopes and expectations King Harold bade his standard be set up a little way down the slope of Senlac hill, at the point where the ascent from the valley was least steep, and on which the fiercest attacks of the advancing enemy were sure to be directed.

On Saturday the fourteenth of October, 1066, was fought the great battle.

The Duke stood on a hill where he could best see his men: the barons surrounded him, and he spoke to them proudly. He told them how he trusted them, and how all that he gained should be theirs; and how sure he felt of conquest, for in all the world there was not so brave an army or such good men and true as were then forming about him. "Spare not," he cried; "strike hard at the beginning; stay not to take spoil. There will be no safety in

asking quarter or in flight. You may flee to the
sea, but you can flee no farther; you will find neither
ships nor bridge there; and the English will over-
take you there and slay you in your shame. Then,
as flight will not secure you, fight, and you will
conquer. We are come for glory, the victory is in
our hands, and we can make sure of obtaining it,
if we so please."

The English had built up a fence before them with
their shields, and with ash and other wood, and
had joined the whole work so as not to leave even a
crevice, and thus they had a barricade on their front
through which any Norman who would attack them
must first pass. Being covered in this way, their aim
was to defend themselves; and if they had remained
steady for that purpose they would not have been
conquered, for every Norman who made his way
in lost his life.

At length the Normans appeared advancing over
a ridge, and the first division of their troops moved
onwards across the valley. And presently another
division, still larger, came in sight, and were led
to another part of the field. The third company
covered all the plain, and in the midst of them was
raised a standard which came from Rome, and which
the Pope had sent to William.

Then Taillefer, the minstrel, who sang right well,
rode mounted on a swift horse before the Duke,
singing of Charlemagne, and of Roland, of Oliver,
and the Peers who died at Roncesvalles.

And when they drew nigh to the English, " A boon, sire ! " cried Taillefer : " I have long served you, and you owe me for all such service. I ask as my reward, and beseech you for it earnestly, that you will allow me to strike the first blow in the battle ! " The Duke answered, " I grant it ! " Then Taillefer put his horse to the gallop, charging before all the rest, and struck an Englishman dead. Then he drew his sword, and struck another, crying out, " Come on, come on ! " At the second blow he struck, the English surrounded him and slew him.

Forthwith arose the noise and cry of war. Loud and far resounded the bray of the trumpets, and the shocks of the lances, the quick clashing of swords, the shouts of the victors, and the groans and cries of the dying. The Normans pressed on to the assault, and the English defended their post right well.

In the plain was a ditch, which the Normans now had behind them. But the English charged, and drove the Normans before them till they made them fall back upon this ditch, overthrowing into it both horses and men. Many fell therein, rolling one over the other, with their faces to the earth, unable to rise. At no time during the battle did so many Normans die as perished in that fosse.

Then Duke William's brother, Odo, the Bishop of Bayeux, galloped up, and said to them : " Stand fast ! stand fast ! " So they took courage, and remained where they were.

There, from nine o'clock in the morning, when the combat began, till three o'clock came, the fight was up and down, this way and that, and no one knew who would conquer. Both sides stood so firm and fought so well that no one could guess which would prevail.   The Norman archers with their bows shot thickly upon the English ; but they covered themselves with their shields, so that the arrows could not reach their bodies.   Then the Normans determined to shoot their arrows upwards into the air, so that they might fall on their enemies' heads, and strike their faces.   When they aimed so, the arrows in falling struck their heads, and put out the eyes of many.   They flew thicker than rain before the wind.

Then it was that an arrow, that had been thus shot upwards, struck Harold above his right eye, and put it out.   In his agony he drew the arrow and threw it away, breaking it with his hands : and the pain in his head was so great that he leaned upon his shield.

When the Normans saw that the English defended themselves well, and were so strong in their position that little could be done against them, they arranged to draw off, and to pretend to flee, till the English should pursue and scatter themselves over the field : for they saw that, if they could once get their enemies to break their ranks, they might be attacked more easily.

Therefore the Normans by little and little fled,

and the English began to follow them. Great mischief thereby befell them ; for if they had not moved,
it is not likely that they would have been conquered.
When the Normans had so retreated for a space,
and numbers of the English had come out to pursue
them, they turned their faces towards the foe again,
and the fury of the battle redoubled.

Now indeed might be heard the roar and the noise
of many men fighting. The Normans once more
approached the barricade, and began to hew it down
with their swords, and the English in great trouble
fell back upon their standard, where were collected
the wounded. Duke William himself pressed close
upon them, striving to reach the standard with the
great troop which he led.

One of the English was a man of great strength,
and was armed with a hatchet. All feared him,
for he had struck down a great many Normans.
The Duke spurred on his horse, and aimed a blow
at him, but he stooped and so escaped the stroke.
Then, jumping to one side, he lifted his hatchet aloft,
and struck the Duke on the head, beating in his helmet.
William was very near to falling, but recovered
himself with an effort.

Loud was now the clamour, and great the slaughter ;
many a soul then quitted the body which it inhabited.
The living marched over heaps of the dead, and
each side was weary of striking. He charged on
who could, and he who could no longer strike still
pushed forward. Sad was his fate who fell in the

midst, for he had little chance of rising again, and many in truth fell who never rose at all, being crushed under the throng.

The Saxon lifted his hatchet aloft and struck the Duke on the head.

And now the Normans had pressed on so far that at last they had reached the standard. There Harold had remained, defending himself to the utmost; but he was sore wounded in his eye by the arrow, and suffered grievous pain from the blow. An armed man came in the throng of the battle, and struck him on his helmet, and beat him to the ground; and as he sought to recover himself, a knight beat him down again, striking him on the thick of his thigh, down to the bone.

His brother Gurth saw the English falling around, and that there was no remedy. He saw his race hastening to ruin, and despaired of any aid; he would have fled but could not, for the throng continually increased. And the Duke pushed on till he reached him, and struck him with great force. And he fell, and rose no more.

The golden standard was beaten down and taken, and Harold and the best of his friends were slain. But there was so much eagerness, and throng of so many around, seeking to kill him, that it is not known who slew him.

The English were in great trouble at having lost their king, and at the Duke's having conquered and beaten down the standard; but still they fought on, and defended themselves long, and in fact till the day drew to a close. Then it clearly appeared to all that the standard was lost, and the news spread throughout the army that Harold for certain was dead; and all saw that there was no longer any hope, so they left the field, and those fled who could.

If Harold, or either of his brothers, had survived, the remains of the English army might have formed again in the wood, and could at least have effected an orderly retreat, and prolonged the war. But Gurth and Leofwine, and all the bravest thanes of southern England, lay dead on Senlac around their fallen king.

Many a legend was told in after years respecting the discovery and the burial of the corpse of Harold. The Norman soldiery and camp-followers had stripped and gashed the slain, and it was long before, among the mutilated and gory heaps, the features of the king could be recognised.

His mother sought the victorious Norman, and begged the dead body of her son. William at first answered her, in his wrath and in the hardness of his heart, that a man who had been false to his word should have no other grave than the sand of the shore. He added, with a sneer, "Harold mounted guard on the coast while he was alive; he may continue his guard now he is dead." A grave washed by the

THE BAYEUX TAPESTRY.

Round the nave of the Cathedral of Bayeux, in Normandy, is a great tapestry, which tells the story of the Battle of Hastings. The picture below is taken from it, and represents the Norman cavalry attacking the English. On the title-page of this book is another which shows the death of Harold's brothers.

spray of the Sussex waves would have been the noblest burial-place for the martyr of Saxon freedom. But Harold's mother was urgent in her lamentations and her prayers, the conquerer relented, and the remains of King Harold were deposited in Waltham Abbey.

On Christmas day of the same year, William the Conqueror was crowned, at London, King of England.

Exercises.

I.

1. How did William compel Harold to promise that he would help him to become King of England?
2. Where did the Normans land?
3. Describe the ground on which the Battle of Hastings was fought.
4. How was it that the English spies mistook the Norman soldiers for priests?
5. In what way had the English protected themselves?
6. Tell the story of the death of Taillefer.
7. What was the device of the Norman archers through which Harold was wounded by an arrow?
8. How did the Norman soldiers induce the English to forsake their strong position?
9. What do you think was the chief cause of the Normans winning the battle?
10. Describe the death of Harold.
11. Where was Harold buried?

II.

1. Join the following sentences in such a way as to make a good paragraph, and then compare your result with the original piece on p. 180.

" The English king halted. He was about seven miles from the Norman lines. He sent some spies to examine the number and preparations of the enemy. The spies returned. They related with astonishment that there were more priests in William's camp than there were fighting men in the English army. They had mistaken the Norman soldiers for priests. The Norman soldiers cut their hair and shaved their chins. Harold smiled at their words. He knew the Norman usages."

2. What were the actual words used by William in the following passage

" The Duke told his barons how he trusted them, and how all that he gained should be theirs : and that he felt sure of conquest, for in all the world there was not so brave an army or such good men and true as were then forming about him. He told them to strike and spare not, and said that they had come for glory and could take the victory, if they so pleased."

III.

Describe the pictures on pages 186 and 188.

On September the 21st, 1741, being then on a visit and intent on field-sports, I rose before day-break: when I came into the enclosures, I found the stubbles and clover-grounds matted all over with a thick coat of cobweb, in the meshes of which a copious and heavy dew hung so plentifully that the whole face of the country seemed, as it were, covered with two or three nets drawn one over another. When the dogs attempted to hunt, their eyes were so blinded and hoodwinked that they could not proceed, but were obliged to lie down and scrape the cobwebs from their faces with their fore-feet, so that, finding my sport interrupted, I returned home musing in my mind on the oddness of the occurrence.

As the morning advanced, the sun became bright and warm, and the day turned out one of those most

M

lovely ones which no season but the autumn produces ; cloudless, calm, serene, and worthy of the
South of France itself.

About nine an appearance very unusual began to
demand our attention, a shower of cobwebs falling
from very elevated regions, and continuing, without
any interruption, till the close of the day. These
webs were not single filmy threads, floating in the
air in all directions, but perfect flakes or rags : some
near an inch broad, and five or six long, which fell
with a speed which showed that they were considerably heavier than the air.

On every side as the observer turned his eyes he
beheld fresh flakes falling into his sight, and twinkling
like stars as they turned their sides towards the
sun.

How far this wonderful shower extended would
be difficult to say : but we know that it reached
Bradley, Selborne, and Alresford, three places which
lie in a sort of triangle, the shortest of whose sides
is about eight miles in extent.

At the second of those places there was a gentleman who observed it the moment he got abroad ;
but concluded that, as soon as he came upon the
hill above his house, where he took his morning
rides, he should be higher than this shower, which
he imagined might have been blown, like thistle-
down, from the common above : but, to his great
astonishment, when he rode to the most elevated
part of the down, 300 feet above his fields, he found

the webs in appearance still as much above him as before ; still descending into sight, and tumbling in the sun so as to draw the attention of the dullest person.

Neither before nor after was any such fall observed ; but on this day the flakes hung on the trees and hedges so thick that a person sent out might have gathered baskets full.

The remark that I shall make on these cobweb-like appearances, called gossamer, is that, strange as the notions about them were formerly, nobody in these days doubts but that they are the real production of small spiders, which swarm in the fields in fine weather in autumn, and have a power of shooting out webs from their tails so as to render themselves lighter than air.

But why these wingless insects should that day take such a wonderful excursion, and why their webs should at once become so heavy as to be considerably more weighty than air, and to descend with such quickness, is a matter beyond my skill. If I might be allowed to hazard a guess, I should imagine that those filmy threads, when first shot, might be entangled in the rising dew, and so drawn up, spiders and all, by a brisk evaporation into the region where clouds are formed : and if the spiders have a power of coiling and thickening their webs in the air, then, when they were become heavier than air, they must fall.

Every day in fine weather, in autumn chiefly, do
I see those spiders shooting out their webs, and
mounting aloft : they will go off from your finger
if you will take them into your hand. Last summer
one alighted on my book as I was reading in the
parlour ; and, running to the top of the page, and
shooting out a web, took its departure from thence.
But what I most wondered at, was that it went off
with considerable speed in a place where no air was
stirring ; and I am sure that I did not assist it with
my breath. So that these little crawlers seem to
have, while mounting, some power of flying without
the use of wings, and to move in the air faster than
the air itself.

(Gilbert White's "Natural History of Selborne.")

Exercises.
I.
1. What is Gossamer ? What does it look like ?
How is it made ? At what time of the year
is it seen ?
2. At what time of day did the author of this piece
go out into the fields ?
3. How widely did the shower of Gossamer extend ?

II.
1. Find rhymes for the following words :—
Field, dew, face, drawn, sport, bright, shower,
float, long, observe, swarm, quick, day,
mountain, speed.
2. Write out this piece as a poem by dividing it into
lines at the proper places :—

1 wandered lonely as a cloud that floats on high o'er vales and hills, when all at once I saw a crowd, a host of golden Daffodils ; beside the lake, beneath the trees, fluttering and dancing in the breeze. Continuous as the stars that shine and twinkle in the Milky Way, they stretched in never-ending line along the margin of a bay : ten thousand saw I at a glance, tossing their heads in sprightly dance. The waves beside them danced, but they out-did the sparkling waves in glee : a Poet could not but be gay in such a jocund company. I gazed, and gazed, but little thought what wealth the show to me had brought. For oft, when on my couch I lie, in vacant or in pensive mood, they flash upon that inward eye that is the bliss of solitude ; and then my heart with pleasure fills, and dances with the Daffodils.

III.

1. Have you ever seen a spider's web on a misty morning ? Describe its appearance.

2. Imagine yourself to be in a field where there are many dandelions whose heads are covered with thistle-down. A gentle breeze is blowing the down away. Describe the appearance of the field.

HOW MR PICKWICK AND MR WINKLE DISPORTED THEMSELVES ON THE ICE

(Adapted from Dickens' "The Pickwick Papers.")

"Well, Sam," said Mr. Pickwick, as that favoured servant entered his bedchamber with his warm water, on the morning of Christmas Day, "Still frosty?"

"Water in the wash-hand basin's a mask o' ice, sir," responded Sam.

"Severe weather, Sam," observed Mr. Pickwick, "I shall be down in a quarter of an hour."

In the morning the whole party, consisting of Mr. Wardle, the host, Mr. Benjamin Allen and Mr. Bob Sawyer, two medical students, Miss Arabella Allen and Miss Emily Wardle, Messrs. Snodgrass, Winkle, Tupman and Pickwick, went to church. On their return, they did more than justice to a substantial lunch.

" Now," said Wardle, after lunch was over, " what do you say to an hour on the ice ? We shall have plenty of time."

" Capital ! " said Mr. Benjamin Allen.

" Prime ! " ejaculated Mr. Bob Sawyer.

" You skate, of course, Winkle ? " said Wardle,

" Ye—yes ; oh, yes," replied Mr. Winkle. " I—I— am *rather* out of practice."

" Oh, *do* skate, Mr. Winkle," said Arabella. " I like to see it so much."

" Oh, it is *so* graceful," said another young lady.

A third young lady said it was elegant, and a fourth expressed her opinion that it was " swan- like."

" I should be very happy, I am sure," said Mr. Winkle, reddening ; " but I have no skates."

His objection was at once over-ruled. Trundle had a couple of pairs, and the fat boy announced that there were half-a-dozen more downstairs : whereat Mr. Winkle expressed exquisite delight, and looked exquisitely uncomfortable.

Old Wardle led the way to a large sheet of ice ; and the fat boy and Mr. Weller having shovelled and swept away the snow which had fallen on it during the night, Mr. Bob Sawyer adjusted his skates with a dexterity which to Mr. Winkle was perfectly mar- vellous, and described circles with his left leg, and cut figures of eight, and inscribed upon the ice, without once stopping for breath, a great many other pleasant and astonishing devices, to the excessive satisfaction of Mr. Pickwick, Mr. Tupman and the ladies ; which reached a pitch of positive enthusiasm, when old Wardle and Benjamin Allen, assisted by the aforesaid Bob Sawyer, performed some mystic evolutions, which they called a reel.

All this time Mr. Winkle, with his face and hands blue with cold, had been forcing a gimlet into the soles of his feet, and putting his skates on with the points behind, and getting the straps into a very complicated and entangled state, with the assist-ance of Mr. Snodgrass, who knew rather less about skates than a Hindoo. At length, however, with the assistance of Mr. Weller, the unfortunate skates were firmly screwed and buckled on, and Mr. Winkle was raised to his feet.

"Now, then, sir," said Sam, in an encouraging tone ; "off with you, and show 'em how to do it."

"Stop, Sam, stop !" said Mr. Winkle, trembling violently, and clutching hold of Sam's arms with the grasp of a drowning man. "How slippery it is, Sam !"

"Not an uncommon thing upon ice, sir !" replied Mr. Weller. "Hold up, sir !"

This last observation of Mr. Weller's bore refer-ence to a demonstration Mr. Winkle made, at that instant, of a frantic desire to throw his feet in the air, and dash the back of his head on the ice.

"These—these—are very awkward skates : aren't they, Sam ?" inquired Mr. Winkle, staggering.

"I 'm afeerd there 's a orkard gen'l'm'n in 'em, sir," replied Sam.

"Now, Winkle," cried Mr. Pickwick, quite unconscious that there was anything the matter. "Come : the ladies are all anxiety."

"Yes, yes," replied Mr. Winkle, with a ghastly smile. "I 'm coming."

"Just a-goin' to begin," said Sam, endeavouring to disengage himself. "Now, sir, start off!"

"Stop an instant, Sam," gasped Mr. Winkle,

clinging most affectionately to Mr. Weller. "I find I 've got a couple of coats at home that I don't want, Sam. You may have them, Sam."

"Thank'ee, sir," replied Mr. Weller.

"Never mind touching your hat, Sam," said Mr. Winkle, hastily. "You needn't take your hand away to do that. I meant to have given you five shillings this morning for a Christmas box, Sam. I 'll give it you this afternoon, Sam."

"You 're wery good, sir," replied Mr. Weller.

"Just hold me at first, Sam, will you ? " said Mr. Winkle. "There—that 's right. I shall soon get in the way of it, Sam. Not too fast, Sam : not too fast."

Mr. Winkle, stooping forward, with his body half doubled up, was being assisted over the ice by Mr. Weller, in a very singular and un-swan-like manner, when Mr. Pickwick most innocently shouted from the opposite bank :

"Sam ! "

"Sir ? "

"Here. I want you."

"Let go, sir," said Sam. "Don't you hear the governor a-callin' ? Let go, sir."

With a violent effort, Mr. Weller disengaged himself from the grasp of the agonized Mr. Winkle, to whom, in so doing, he administered a considerable impetus. With an accuracy which no degree of dexterity or practice could have ensured, the unfortunate gentleman bore swiftly down into the

centre of the reel, at the very moment when Mr.
Bob Sawyer was performing a flourish of unparalleled
beauty. Mr. Winkle struck wildly against him, and
with a loud crash they both fell heavily down.

Mr. Winkle bore swiftly down into the reel.

Mr. Pickwick ran to the spot. Bob Sawyer had
risen to his feet, but Mr. Winkle was far too wise
to do anything of the kind—in skates. He was seated
on the ice, making spasmodic efforts to smile : but

anguish was depicted on every lineament of his countenance.

"Are you hurt?" inquired Mr. Benjamin Allen, with great anxiety.

"Not much," said Mr. Winkle, rubbing his back very hard.

Mr. Pickwick was excited and indignant. He beckoned to Mr. Weller, and said in a stern voice, "Take his skates off."

"No: but really I had scarcely begun," remonstrated Mr. Winkle.

"Take his skates off," repeated Mr. Pickwick firmly.

The command was not to be resisted. Mr. Winkle allowed Sam to obey in silence.

"Lift him up," said Mr. Pickwick. Sam assisted him to rise. Mr. Pickwick retired a few paces apart from the by-standers; and, beckoning his friend to approach, fixed a searching look upon him, and uttered in a low, but distinct and emphatic tone, these remarkable words:

"You're a humbug, sir."

"A what?" said Mr. Winkle, starting.

"A humbug sir. I will speak plainer, if you wish it. An impostor, sir."

With these words, Mr. Pickwick turned slowly on his heel, and rejoined his friends.

While Mr. Pickwick was delivering himself of the sentiment just recorded, Mr. Weller and the fat boy, having by their joint endeavours cut out a slide, were exercising themselves thereupon, in a very masterly and brilliant manner. It was a good long slide, and there was something in the motion which Mr. Pickwick, who was very cold with standing still, could not help envying.

" It looks a nice warm exercise, that, doesn't it ? " he inquired of Wardle, when that gentleman was thoroughly out of breath, by reason of the manner in which he had converted his legs into a pair of compasses, and drawn complicated problems on the ice.

" Ah, it does indeed," replied Wardle. " Do you slide ? "

" I used to do so, on the gutters, when I was a boy," replied Mr. Pickwick.

" Try it now," said Wardle.

" Oh, do, please, Mr. Pickwick ! " cried all the ladies.

" I should be very happy to afford you any amusement," replied Mr. Pickwick, " but I haven't done such a thing these thirty years."

" Pooh ! pooh ! nonsense ! " said Wardle, dragging off his skates with the impetuosity which characterized all his proceedings. " Here ; I 'll keep you company : come along ! " and away went the good-tempered old fellow down the slide, with a rapidity which came very close upon Mr. Weller, and beat the fat boy all to nothing.

Mr. Pickwick paused ; considered ; pulled off his gloves and put them in his hat : took two or three runs, baulked himself as often, and at last took another run, and went slowly and gravely down the slide, with his feet about a yard and a-quarter apart, amidst the gratified shouts of all the spectators.

"Keep the pot a-boilin', sir!" said Sam; and down went Wardle again, and then Mr. Pickwick, and then Sam, and then Mr. Winkle, and then Mr. Bob Sawyer, and then the fat boy, and then Mr. Snodgrass, following closely upon each other's heels, and running after each other with as much eagerness as if all their future prospects in life depended on their expedition.

The sport was at its height, the sliding was at its quickest, the laughter was at its loudest, when a sharp smart crack was heard. There was a quick rush towards the bank, a wild scream from the ladies, and a shout from Mr. Tupman. A large mass of ice disappeared : the water bubbled up over it : Mr. Pickwick's hat, gloves, and handkerchief were floating on the surface ; and this was all of Mr. Pickwick that anybody could see.

Dismay and anguish were depicted on every countenance, the males turned pale, and the females fainted ; Mr. Snodgrass and Mr. Winkle grasped each other by the hand ; while Mr. Tupman, by way of rendering the promptest assistance, and at the same time conveying to any persons who might be within hearing the clearest possible notion of the catastrophe, ran off across the country at his utmost speed, screaming "Fire!" with all his might.

It was at this moment that a face, head, and shoulders, emerged from beneath the water, and

disclosed the features and spectacles of Mr. Pickwick.

"Do you feel the bottom there, old fellow?" said Wardle.

"Yes, certainly," replied Mr. Pickwick, wringing the water from his head and face, and gasping for breath. "I fell upon my back. I couldn't get on my feet at first."

The clay upon so much of Mr. Pickwick's coat as was visible bore testimony to the accuracy of this statement; and as the fears of the spectators were still further relieved by the fat boy's suddenly recollecting that the water was nowhere more than five feet deep, prodigies of valour were performed to get him out. After a vast quantity of splashing,

and cracking, and struggling, Mr. Pickwick was at
length fairly extricated from his unpleasant position,
and once more stood on dry land.

" Oh, he 'll catch his death of cold," said Emily.

" Dear old thing ! " said Arabella. " Let me wrap
this shawl round you, Mr. Pickwick."

" Ah, that 's the best thing you can do," said Wardle:
"and when you' ve got it on, run home as fast as
your legs can carry you, and jump into bed directly."

A dozen shawls were offered on the instant.   Three
or four of the thickest having been selected, Mr.
Pickwick was wrapped up, and started off, presenting
the singular sight of an elderly gentleman, dripping
wet, and without a hat, with his arms bound down
to his sides, skimming over the ground at the rate
of six good English miles an hour.

Urged on by Sam Weller, he kept at the very top
of his speed until he reached the door of Manor Farm,
where Mr. Tupman had arrived some five minutes
before, and had frightened the old lady of the house
into palpitation of the heart by impressing upon her
the belief that the kitchen chimney was on fire.

Mr. Pickwick paused not an instant until he was
snug in bed. Sam Weller lighted a blazing fire in
the room, and took up his dinner. A bowl of punch
was carried up afterwards, and when Mr. Pickwick
awoke the next morning, there was not a sign of
rheumatism about him.

Exercises.
I.

1. On what day of the year did the events in this story take place ?
2. Who were members of the party that went skating ?
3. Who helped Mr. Winkle to put on his skates ?
4. Why did Mr. Winkle give Sam Weller five shillings ?
5. What was the cause of Mr. Winkle's collision with Bob Sawyer ?
6. Why did Mr. Pickwick tell Mr. Winkle that he was a humbug ?
7. Describe Mr. Wardle.

II.

1. Make as many words as you can with the following :—

[Model : break—breakfast, breakwater, breakneck.] :
—Tree—, wind—, stream—, —fall, —work, —house.

2. What is the meaning of ?—Respond, device, dexterity, marvellous, unfortunate, frantic, practice, countenance, indignant, distinct, brilliant, spectator, catastrophe, valour.

III.

1. Tell this story in your own words, using the following headings :—
    1. Mr. Pickwick and his friends go skating.
    2. Mr. Winkle, with the assistance of Sam Weller, puts on his skates.
    3. Mr. Winkle collides with Bob Sawyer.
    4. Mr. Winkle's skates are taken off.
    5. Mr. Pickwick slides.
    6. Mr. Pickwick falls through the ice.
    7. Mr. Pickwick is rescued and returns home.
2. Give Mr. Pickwick's account of his adventures on the ice.

N

WINTER

When icicles hang by the wall,
And Dick the shepherd blows his nail,
And Tom bears logs into the hall,
And milk comes frozen home in pail;
When blood is nipped, and ways be foul,
Then nightly sings the staring owl
    "Tu-whu!
Tu-whit, tu-whu!"—a merry note,
While greasy Joan doth keel[1] the pot.

When all aloud the wind doth blow,
And coughing drowns the parson's saw[2],
And birds sit brooding in the snow,
And Marian's nose looks red and raw,
When roasted crabs[3] hiss in the bowl,
Then nightly sings the staring owl
    "Tu-whu!
Tu-whit, tu-whu!"—a merry note,
While greasy Joan doth keel the pot.

William Shakespeare.

(1) cool.   (2) sermon.   (3) crab-apples.

AN ADVENTURE with SMUGGLERS

R. EADIE

(Reprinted from "Micah Clarke," by Sir Arthur Conan Doyle, by permission
of the author and Messrs. Longmans, Green & Co.)

I.

It was a blithesome morning. The sun was rising
over the distant hills, and heaven and earth were
ruddy and golden. The trees in the wayside orchards
were full of swarms of birds, who chattered and
sang until the air was full of their piping. There
was lightsomeness and gladness in every breath.
The wistful-eyed red Somerset kine stood along
by the hedge-rows, casting great shadows down
the fields and gazing at me as I passed. Farm horses

leaned over wooden gates, and snorted a word of greeting to the glossy-coated brother whom I bestrode. A great herd of snowy-fleeced sheep streamed toward us over the hillside and frisked and gambolled in the sunshine. All was innocent life, from the lark which sang on high to the little shrew-mouse which ran amongst the ripening corn, or the martin which dashed away at the sound of my approach.

From the high ground to the north I looked back upon the sleeping town, with the broad edging of tents and waggons, which showed how suddenly its population had outgrown it. The Royal Standard still fluttered from the Tower of St. Mary Magdalene, while close by its beautiful brother-turret of St. James bore aloft the blue flag of Monmouth. As I gazed the quick, petulant roll of a drum rose up on the still morning air, with the clear ringing call of the bugles summoning the troops from their slumbers.

Beyond the town, and on either side of it, stretched a glorious view of the Somersetshire downs, rolling away to the distant sea, with town and hamlet, castle turret and church tower, wooded coombe and stretch of grain-land,—as fair a scene as the eye could wish to rest upon. As I wheeled my horse and sped upon my way I felt that this was a land worth fighting for, and that a man's life was a small thing if he could but aid, in however trifling a degree, in working out its freedom and its happiness.

At a little village over the hill I fell in with an outpost of horse, the commander of which rode some distance with me.

It seemed strange to my Hampshire eyes to note that the earth is all red in these parts. The cows, too, are mostly red.

My course ran along by the foot of the beautiful Quantock Hills, where heavy-wooded coombes are scattered over the broad heathery downs, deep with bracken and whortlebushes. On either side of the track steep winding glens sloped downwards, lined with yellow gorse, which blazed out from the deep-red soil like a flame from embers. Peat-coloured streams splashed down the valleys and over the road, through which Covenant ploughed fetlock-deep, and shied to see the broad-backed trout darting from between his fore-feet.

All day I rode through this beautiful country, meeting few folk, for I kept away from the main roads. A black jack of ale and the heel of a loaf at a wayside inn were all my refreshments. It was not until evening that I at last came out upon the banks of the Bristol Channel, at the place where the muddy Parret makes its way into the sea.

At this point the channel is so broad that the Welsh mountains can scarcely be distinguished. The shore is flat and black and oozy, flecked over with white patches of sea-birds, but farther to the east there rises a line of hills, very wild and rugged, rising in places into steep precipices. The road wound over these bleak and rocky hills, which are sparsely inhabited by a wild race of fishermen, or shepherds.

As the night drew in the country became bleaker and more deserted. An occasional light twinkling in the distance from some lonely hillside cottage was the only sign of the presence of man. The rough track still skirted the sea, and, high as it was, the spray from the breakers drifted across it. The salt prinkled on my lips, and the air was filled with the hoarse roar of the surge and the thin piping of curlews, which flitted past in the darkness like white, shadowy, sad-voiced creatures from some other world. The wind blew in short, quick, angry puffs from the westward, and far out on the black waters a single glimmer of light rising and falling, tossing up, and then sinking out of sight, showed how fierce a sea had risen in the channel.

Riding through the gloaming in this strange wild scenery, my mind naturally turned towards the past. I thought of my father and my mother, of the state of the army and the prospects of the rebellion. Turning over all these things in my mind I began to doze upon my horse's back, overcome by the fatigue of the journey and the drowsy lullaby of the waves, when in an instant, without warning, I was dashed violently from my horse, and left lying half-conscious on the stony track.

So stunned and shaken was I by the sudden fall that, though I had a dim knowledge of shadowy figures bending over me, and of hoarse laughter sounding in my ears, I could not tell for a moment where I was nor what had befallen me. When at last I did make an attempt to recover my feet I found that a loop of rope had been slipped round my arms and my legs so as to secure them. With a hard struggle I got one hand free, and dashed it in the face of one of the men who were holding me down; but the whole gang of a dozen or more set upon me at once, and while some thumped and kicked at me, others tied a fresh cord round my elbows, and deftly fastened it in such a way as to pinion me completely. Finding that in my weak and dazed state all efforts were of no avail, I lay sullen and watchful, taking no heed of the random blows which were still showered upon me. So dark was it that I could neither see the faces of my attackers, nor form any guess as to who they might be, or how they had hurled me from my saddle. The champing and stamping of my horse hard by showed me that Covenant was a prisoner as well as his master.

"Dutch Pete's got as much as he can carry," said a rough, harsh voice. "He lies on the track as limp as a conger."

"Ah, poor Pete!" muttered another. "He'll never deal a card or drain a glass of the right Cognac again."

"There you lie, mine goot vriend," said the injured man, in weak, quavering tones. "And I will prove to you that you lie if you have a flask in your pocket."

As he spoke the edge of the moon peeped over a cliff and threw a flood of cold clear light upon the scene. Looking up I saw that a strong rope had been tied across the road from one tree trunk to another, about eight feet above the ground. This could not have been seen by me, even had I been fully awake, in the dusk ; but, catching me across the breast as Covenant trotted under it, it had swept me off and dashed me with great force to the ground. Either the fall or the blows which I had received had cut me badly, for I could feel the blood trickling in a warm stream past my ear and down my neck.

The gang who had seized me were rough-bearded fellows in fur caps and fustian jackets, with buff belts round their waists, from which hung short straight swords. Their dark sun-dried faces and their great boots marked them as fishermen or sea-men, as might be guessed from their rude sailor speech. A pair knelt on either side with their hands upon my arms, a third stood behind with a cocked pistol pointed at my head, while the others, seven or eight in number, were helping to his feet the man whom I had struck, who was bleeding freely from a cut over the eye.

"Take the horse up to Daddy Mycroft's," said a stout, black-bearded man, who seemed to be their leader. "It is no mere hack, but a comely, full-blooded brute, which will fetch sixty pieces at the least. Your share of that, Peter, will buy plaster for your cut."

"Ha," cried the Dutchman, shaking his fist at me, " You would strike Peter, would you ? You would draw Peter's blood, would you ? Man, if you and I were together upon the hillside we should see vich vas the petter man."

"Slack your jaw tackle, Pete," growled one of his comrades. "This fellow is a limb of Satan for sure, and doth follow a calling that none but a mean, snivelling, baseborn son of a gun would take to. Yet I warrant, from the look of him, that he could truss you like a woodcock if he had his great hands upon you."

"Truss me, would he?" cried the other, whom the blow and the brandy had driven to madness. "We shall see. Take that! take that!" He ran at me, and kicked me as hard as he could with his heavy sea-boots.

Some of the gang laughed, but the man who had spoken before gave the Dutchman a shove that sent him whirling. "None of that," he said sternly. "We'll have British fair-play on British soil. I won't stand by and see an Englishman kicked, d'ye see, by a chicken-hearted Amsterdamer. Hang him, if the skipper likes. That's all above board. But, if it's a fight that you will have, touch that man again."

"All right, Dicon," said their leader soothingly. "We all know that Pete's not a fighting man, but he's the best cooper on the coast, eh, Pete?"

"Oh, you remember that, Captain Murgatroyd," said the Dutchman sulkily. "But you see me knocked about, and bullied, and called names."

"Enough said!" the Captain answered. "Up

with the prisoner, and let us get him safely into the bilboes."

I was raised to my feet and half carried, half dragged along in the midst of the gang. My horse had already been led away in the opposite direction. Our course lay off the road, down a very rocky and rugged ravine which sloped away towards the sea. There seemed to be no trace of a path, and I could only stumble along over rocks and bushes as best I might in my crippled and fettered state. The blood, however, had dried over my wounds, and the cool sea breeze playing upon my forehead refreshed me, and helped me to take a clearer view of my position.

It was plain from their talk that these men were smugglers. But I could not but wonder, as I was dragged along, what had led them to lie in wait for me as they had done. The road along which I had travelled was a lonely one, and yet a fair number of travellers bound from the West through Weston to Bristol must use it. The gang could not lie in perpetual guard over it. Why had they set a trap on this particular night, then? The smugglers were a lawless and desperate body, but they did not, as a rule, descend to robbery. As long as no one interfered with them they were seldom the first to break the peace. Then, why had they lain in wait for me, who had never injured them?

I was still turning these questions over in my mind when we all came to a halt, and the Captain blew a shrill note on a whistle that hung round his neck.

II.

The place where we found ourselves was the darkest and most rugged spot in the whole wild gorge. On either side great cliffs shot up, which arched over our heads, with a fringe of ferns and bracken on either lip, so that the dark sky and the few twinkling stars were well-nigh hid. Great black rocks loomed vaguely out in the shadowy light, while in front a high tangle of what seemed to be brushwood barred our road.

At a second whistle, however, a glint of light was seen through the branches, and the whole mass was swung to one side as though it moved upon a hinge. Beyond it a dark winding passage opened into the side of the hill, down which we went with our backs bowed, for the rock ceiling was of no great height. On every side of us sounded the throbbing of the sea.

Passing through the entrance, which must have been dug with great labour through the solid rock, we came out into a lofty and roomy cave, lit up by a fire at one end, and by several torches. By their smoky yellow glare I could see that the roof was at least fifty feet above us, and was hung with long lime-crystals, which sparkled and gleamed with great brightness. The floor of the cave was formed of fine sand, as soft and velvety as a Wilton carpet, sloping down in a way which showed that the cave must at its mouth open upon the sea, which was

A Smugglers' Cave.

confirmed by the booming and splashing of the waves, and by the fresh salt air which filled the whole cavern. No water could be seen, however, as a sharp turn cut off our view of the outlet.

In this rock-girt space, which may have been sixty paces long and thirty across, there were gathered great piles of casks, kegs, and cases; muskets, cutlasses, staves, cudgels, and straw were littered about the floor. At one end a high wood fire blazed merrily, casting strange shadows along the walls, and sparkling like a thousand diamonds among the crystals on the roof. The smoke was carried away through a great cleft in the rocks. Seated on boxes, or stretched on the sand round the fire, there were seven or eight more of the band, who sprang to their feet and ran eagerly towards us as we entered.

" Have ye got him ? " they cried. " Did he indeed come ? Had he attendants ? "

" He is here, and he is alone," the Captain answered. " Our hawser fetched him off his horse as neatly as ever a gull was netted by a cragsman. What have ye done in our absence, Silas ? "

" We have the packs ready for carriage," said the man addressed, a sturdy, weather-beaten seaman of middle age. The silk and lace are done in these squares covered over with sacking. The one I have marked ' yarn,' and the other ' jute.' The baccy is in the flat cases over by the Black Drop there. A plaguy job we had carrying it all out, but here it is ship-shape at last."

"Any signs of the 'Fairy Queen?'" asked the smuggler.

"None. Long John is down at the water's edge looking out for her flash-light."

"We cannot hang the gauger until Venables brings up the 'Fairy Queen,'" said Captain Murgatroyd, "for, after all, it was one of his hands that was snackled. Let him do his own dirty work."

"Wouldn't it be a kindly turn to Captain Venables to chuck the gauger down the Black Drop ere he come?" cried the ruffian Dutchman. "He may have such another job to do for us some day."

"Zounds, man, are you in command or am I?" said the leader angrily. "Bring the prisoner forward to the fire! Now, hark ye, dog of a land-shark: you are as surely a dead man as though you were laid out with the tapers burning. See here"—he lifted a torch, and showed by its red light a great crack in the floor across the far end of the cave— "you can judge of the Black Drop's depth!" he said, raising an empty keg and tossing it over into the yawning gulf. For ten seconds we stood silent before a dull distant clatter told that it had at last reached the bottom.

"It's an easier death than the Devizes gallows!" said one.

"Nay, he shall have the gallows first," a second shouted. "It is but his burial that we are arranging."

"He hath not opened his mouth since we took

him," said the man who was called Dicon. " Is he
a mute, then ? Find your tongue, my fine fellow,
and let us hear what your name is. It would have
been well for you if you had been born dumb, so
that you could not have sworn our comrade's life
away."

" I have been waiting for a civil question after
all this brawling and brabbling," said I. " My
name is Micah Clarke. Now, pray inform me who
ye may be, and by what warrant ye stop peaceful
travellers upon the public highway ? "

" This is our warrant," Murgatroyd answered,
touching the hilt of his cutlass. " As to who we are,
ye know that well enough. Your name is not Clarke,
but Westhouse, or Waterhouse, and you are the same
cursed exciseman who snackled our poor comrade,
Cooper Dick, and swore away his life at Ilchester."

" I swear that you are mistaken," I replied. " I
have never in my life been in these parts before."

" Fine words ! Fine words ! " cried another smuggler. " Gauger or no, you must jump for it, since
you know the secret of our cave."

" Your secret is safe with me," I answered. " But
if ye wish to murder me, I shall meet my fate as a
soldier should. I should have chosen to die on the
field of battle, rather than to lie at the mercy of
such a pack of water-rats in their burrow."

" My faith ! " said Murgatroyd. " This is too
tall talk for a gauger. He bears himself like a soldier,
too. It is possible that in snaring the owl we have

caught the falcon. Yet we had certain token that he would come this way, and on such another horse."

"Call up Long John," suggested the Dutchman. "I vould not give a plug of Trinidado for his word. Long John was with Cooper Dick when he was taken."

"Aye," growled the mate Silas. "He got a wipe over the arm with the gauger's sword. He'll know his face, if any will."

"Call him, then," said Murgatroyd, and presently a long, loose-limbed seaman came up from the mouth of the cave, where he had been on the watch. He wore a red kerchief round his forehead, and a blue jerkin, the sleeve of which he slowly rolled up as he came nigh.

"Where is Gauger Westhouse?" he cried; "he has left his mark on my arm. Rat me, if the scar is healed yet. The sun is on our side of the wall now, gauger. But hullo, mates! who be this that ye have clapped into irons? This is not our man!"

"Not our man!" they cried, with a volley of curses.

"Why, this fellow would make two of the gauger, and leave enough over to fashion a magistrate's clerk. Ye may hang him to make sure, but still he's not the man."

"Yes, hang him!" said Dutch Pete. "Is our cave to be the talk of all the country? Vere is the pretty Maria to go then, vid her silks and her satins, her kegs and her cases? Are we to risk our cave for the sake of this fellow? Besides, has he not broken mine head? Is not that vorth a hemp cravat?"

o

" By your leave, Captain," cried Dicon. " I would say that we are not a gang of padders and michers, but a crew of honest seamen, who harm none but those who harm us. Exciseman Westhouse hath slain Cooper Dick, and it is just that he should die for it: but as to taking this young soldier's life, I 'd as soon think of scuttling the saucy Maria, or of mounting the Jolly Roger at her peak."

" Hark ye, Mister Soldier ! " the Captain said. " What brings you to these parts, and what king do you serve ? for I hear there 's a mutiny broken out, and two skippers claim equal rating in the old British ship."

" I am serving under King Monmouth," I answered, seeing that the question must end in a search, and in finding my papers.

" Under King Monmouth ! " cried the smuggler. " Nay, friend, that rings somewhat false. The good King hath, I hear, too much need of his friends in the south to let an able soldier go wandering along the sea-coast like a Cornish wrecker in a sou'-wester."

" I bear despatches," said I, " from the King's own hand to Henry Duke of Beaufort, at his castle at Badminton. Ye can find them in my inner pocket, but I pray ye not to break the seal, lest it bring discredit upon my mission."

Murgatroyd took out my papers, and looked at the back. " Yes," he continued, " it is marked, as you say, 'From James the Second of England, known lately as the Duke of Monmouth, to Henry

Duke of Beaufort, President of Wales, by the hand of Captain Micah Clarke, of Saxon's regiment of Wiltshire foot.' Cast off the lashings, Dicon. So, Captain, you are a free man once more, and I grieve that we should have unwittingly harmed you. We are good Lutherans to a man, and would rather speed you than hinder you on this mission."

"Could we not indeed help him on his way?" said the mate Silas. "For myself, I don't fear a wet jacket or a tarry hand for the cause, and I doubt not ye are all of my way of thinking."

"Aye, aye," cried Long John. "The King's horse are out beyond Weston, but he could give them the slip if he had the *Maria* under him.

"Well," said Murgatroyd, "how would the plan suit you, Captain?"

"My horse!" I objected.

"It need not stop us. I can rig up a handy horse-stall with my spare spars and the grating. The lugger could be brought up to Dead Man's Edge, and the horse led down to it. Here is some cold junk and biscuit—seaman's fare, Captain—and a glass of the real Jamaica to wash it down, an' thy stomach be not too dainty for rough living."

I seated myself on a barrel by the fire, and stretched my limbs, which were cramped and stiffened by their confinement, while one of the seamen bathed the cut on my head with a wet kerchief, and another laid out some food on a case in front of me. After I had sat and smoked for an hour or so, Silas the mate appeared, and said that the lugger was ready and the horse aboard. A boat was drawn up at the water's edge, on the sand, inside the cave. Bidding Murgatroyd farewell, I stepped into it, while the crew pushed her off and sprang in as she glided into deep water.

I could see by the dim light of the single torch which Murgatroyd held upon the margin, that the roof of the cave sloped sheer down upon us as we sculled slowly out towards the entrance. So low did it come at last that there was only a space of a few feet between it and the water, and we had to bend our heads to avoid the rocks above us. The boatmen gave two strong strokes, and we shot out from under the overhanging ledge, and found our-selves in the open, with the stars shining murkily above us, and the moon showing herself dimly and cloudily through a gathering haze.

Right in front of us was a dark blur, which, as we pulled towards it, took the outline of a large lugger rising and falling with the pulse of the sea. Her tall thin spars and delicate network of cordage towered above us as we glided under the counter, while the creaking of blocks and rattle of ropes showed that she was all ready to glide off upon her journey. Lightly and daintily she rode upon the waters, like some giant seafowl, spreading one white pinion after another in preparation for her flight.

The boatmen ran us alongside and steadied the dinghy while I climbed over the bulwarks on to the deck. In the midst of the after-deck the mariners had built a strong stall, in which my good steed was standing, with a bucket full of oats in front of him. My old friend shoved his nose against my face as I came aboard, and neighed his pleasure at finding his master once more. We were still exchanging caresses when the grizzled head of Silas the mate popped out of the cabin hatchway.

"We are fairly on our way, now, Captain Clarke," said he. "Are you not aweary?"

"I am a little tired," I confessed. "My head is throbbing from the crack I got when that hawser of yours dashed me from my saddle."

"An hour or two of sleep will make you as fresh as a Mother Carey's chicken," said the smuggler. "So you had best come down and turn in."

I descended the steep stairs which led down into the low-roofed cabin of the lugger. On either side a recess in the wall had been fitted up as a couch.

"This is your bed," said he, pointing to one of them. I needed no second invitation, but flinging myself down without undressing, I sank in a few minutes into a dreamless sleep, which neither the gentle motion of the boat nor the clank of feet above my head could break off.

In the morning I was awakened by Silas. "We shall be there in a brace of shakes," he said. "Let us load your ground tier, for there is nothing like starting well trimmed with plenty of ballast in the hold."

Following the sailor's advice, I sat down with him and enjoyed a rude but plentiful meal. By the time we had finished, the lugger had been run into a narrow creek, with shelving sandy banks on either side. With much coaxing and pushing Covenant was induced to take to the water, and swam easily ashore, while I followed in the smuggler's dinghy. A few words of rough, kindly leave-taking were shouted after me; I saw the dinghy return, and the

beautiful craft glided out to sea and faded away once more into the mist which hung over the face of the waters.

I heard afterwards that a troop of horse were making themselves very active in those parts by blocking the roads and seizing all who came that way. And so, while I began by being dashed upon a stony road, beaten, kicked, and finally well-nigh put to death in mistake for another, it ended in my being safely carried to my journey's end, whereas, had I gone by land, it is more than likely that I should have been cut off at Weston.

Exercises.

I.

1. What words are the following made from?

[Model: *gladness* is made from *glad*.] Edging, suddenly, freedom, happiness, beautiful, refreshment, occasional, scenery, shaken, laughter, prisoner, lawless, robbery, darkest, smoky, pleasure, downwards.

2. What words are the following made from?

[Model: *wayside* is made from *way* and *side*.] Hedgerow, seabird, overcome, forehead, brushwood, cragsman, highway, indeed, farewell, outline.

3. Rewrite the following sentences, putting a single word in place of each of the italicized phrases :—
   (1) I sank *in a few minutes* into a dreamless sleep.
   (2) *By the time* we had finished, the lugger had been run into a creek.
   (3) Had I gone by land, I should have been *cut off* at Weston.

(4) It was as fair a scene as the eye could wish to *rest upon.*

(5) At a little village I *fell in with* an outpost of horse.

(6) The hills were inhabited by *a wild race of* fishermen.

(7) I found that all my efforts were *of no avail.*

(8) I have never in my life been *in these parts* before.

(9) I shall meet my fate *as a soldier should.*

II.

Write descriptions of the following :—

1. The view that met Micah Clarke's eyes when he left the town.
2. The road along the cliffs.
3. Dutch Pete.
4. The smugglers' cave.
5. The ship *Maria.*
6. Describe the picture on page 219 : how does this differ from the cave in which Micah Clarke was imprisoned ?

Cupid and Psyche.

(Adapted from Adlington's Translation of Apuleius.)

There was once a certain king who had three fair
daughters. The two elder were most comely, but
no tongue could sufficiently set forth the singular
beauty of the youngest, so that the fame of her
loveliness spread abroad and strangers came from
distant lands to see her. In consequence, the temples
and shrines of Venus, the goddess of love and beauty,
began to be neglected and left solitary. When she
saw this, the goddess was angered, and, calling to
her her winged son Cupid, she bade him avenge
the insults that she had received.

Although Psyche's two sisters were royally
married to two kings, and although she was praised
by all for her beauty, no man had come to woo her;
wherefore her father, suspecting that the gods were
jealous of her, went to the oracle of Apollo and offered
sacrifice there, desiring a husband for her. He
received in return this dreadful answer—

"Let Psyche be clad in black, and taken into the
mountains, away from men : for her husband is
not a man, but a fierce dragon."

The king returned home sorrowfully, and declared
to his wife the miserable fate of Psyche. Then,
in due course, Psyche was arrayed in mourning
garments (as had been commanded), led from her

Cupid and Psyche at the Court of Venus (page 239)

home into the wilderness, and there abandoned.
As soon as she was alone she began to weep and
to tremble with fear, expecting that some monster
would appear to devour her. Instead, however,
a gentle warbling wind carried her down into a
pleasant dell, leaving her upon a grassy bank decked
with fragrant flowers.

The night was warm, and Psyche, falling asleep,
passed the hours of darkness in peace. When the
golden hues of dawn appeared she arose, and
wandered along the bank of a stream that ran
through the valley, till she came to a stately building standing in a green meadow. She was so
delighted with the charm of this place that she entered
without fear. But, though she found every door
open to her touch, she could see no one.

When she had viewed every room, she heard a
voice that said : " Why do you marvel, Psyche,
at these riches ? This house and all it contains
are yours. Rest, while we, your servants, prepare
royal meats and dainty dishes for you." And as
the voice promised, so it was : she was served at
table by unseen hands, while some one invisible
sang sweet music to her.

In the evening, after dark had fallen and all was
still, her unknown husband came to her, and she
lost the last trace of the fear that she had still
entertained for her safety. But in the morning,
before it was light, he departed, and did not return
till nightfall. Thus many days passed and Psyche

was content, except that she began to desire exceedingly to see again her parents and sisters.

They, meanwhile, had not forgotten her, and went early to the hills, to discover what had become of her.

At last Psyche could restrain herself no longer, and told her husband that she would die unless she might see her sisters. She besought him to command the wind to bring them down into the valley, as she herself had been brought, and finally, by her entreaties, she gained his consent, although he was very unwilling. He reminded her that she had never seen him, and told her that her sisters would ask many questions about him, and he warned her solemnly that she should not attempt by any means to see him, because, if she did so, she would be deprived of her happiness.

On the next day the gentle zephyr, finding the sisters searching, carried them down into the valley to Psyche. She embraced them, and showed them all the treasures of her house, where also the invisible servants entertained them in the same way as they had served her. When they had eaten and had seen all that she showed them, their hearts began to be filled with great envy against her, and they continually asked her about her husband, and where he was, so that Psyche was in great difficulty to answer them. At the end of the visit she loaded them with golden ornaments and jewels, and caused them to be carried back as they had come.

After no long time the sisters came again to the valley, and on this occasion they told Psyche once more that the oracle had declared that she should be married to a monster, and at length so wrought upon her that she confessed to them that she had

A gentle warbling wind carried her down (page 233).

never seen her husband, and, moreover, they succeeded in persuading her to endeavour to obtain sight of him.

After their departure, Psyche sat tormented by doubt till evening came, and with it her husband's return. At length, after many hesitations and changes of purpose, she resolved to put into execution her promise to her sisters. Accordingly, in the middle of the night she arose, and lit a lamp and looked upon her husband, and behold it was the God of Love himself! For Cupid, hastening to carry out his mother's wishes, had visited Psyche with the intention of harming her. But when he saw how good and how fair she was, his hatred turned to love and he had resolved to marry her.

At the glorious sight that Cupid presented, Psyche was so startled and overcome that her hand trembled as she leant over him, and a drop of hot oil fell upon the right shoulder of the god, and he awoke. Immediately perceiving that she had been disobedient to his orders, he soared in the air on his pinions, and, without a word to his unhappy wife, he flew away.

Then Psyche fell flat on the ground, and lamented piteously : and when she found that her tears were of no avail, she threw herself into the river that flowed past her dwelling. But the water, not suffering her to be drowned, cast her gently upon the land. After that, taking a little heart, she set out and wandered miserably through the world, seeking for her husband.

When Venus heard what had happened, she sent one of her servants, who seized Psyche and dragged her before the offended goddess. Then Venus took a great quantity of seeds of various sorts, mixed them together in a heap, and said to Psyche : " Separate all these grains one from another, disposing them according to their kinds, and let it be done to my content before night." Psyche made no attempt to begin, for she saw that the task was quite impossible for her to perform. But a great swarm of ants came in, arranged all the seed in order, and ran away again in all haste from her sight.

Next day, when dawn shone forth, Venus called Psyche and said : " Do you see yonder forest, the bushes whereof look close down upon the stream hard by ? There are great sheep with fleece that shines like gold. I command you to go to them and bring me some of their wool." This order Venus gave knowing that the sheep were fierce and would destroy the unhappy girl. But Psyche was warned of her danger by a reed of the river, which also told her that in the cool of the day she could go into the thickets and gather locks of golden fleece which she would find hanging on the briars.

Psyche performed this duty also, to the rage of the goddess, who gave her a third task. This was to go to a high hill, and bring her a cup of water from a spring that flowed out of a rock that was perched on the very summit. When poor Psyche reached the hill she saw that it was exceedingly rugged and slippery, and that on every side lay great dragons, with eyes that never closed in sleep. At this she stood still and wept with despair.

Yet her sorrow did not escape notice, for an eagle swept down on outstretched wings, and taking her bottle in his beak, flew between the dragons, and filled it with the water of the river. Then Psyche joyfully took the bottle and presented it to Venus.

The furious goddess would not even then be appeased, but, smiling cruelly, said : "What ? You seem to me a very witch, because you have so cleverly obeyed my commands. Howbeit you shall do one thing more. Take this box, go down to Hades, and desire Persephone, the Queen of the Dead, to send me a little of her beauty."

Then Psyche understood the end of all her fortune, seeing that all pretence was thrown off, and that she was being driven to destruction. Yet again she was saved. For the stones by the wayside took pity on her, and directed her how to approach Persephone, and how to avoid the innumerable snares that she would encounter during her journey. By means of charms she passed the doleful stream of Styx, and Cerberus, the hideous three-headed dog that guards the gate, and came to the desolate house of Pluto, where Persephone dwells, and delivered to her the message of Venus.

After she had received a portion of Persephone's beauty, she retraced her steps. On the way she said to herself, " Am I not foolish in carrying with me divine beauty, not to take a little for my own face to please my love if I find him again ? " Thus thinking, she opened the box, whereupon there issued out not beauty, but a deadly sleep, which seized upon all her limbs, so that she fell down on the ground as if dead.

But Cupid, not being able to endure the absence of Psyche, took his flight from heaven to her, and, wiping away the sleep from her face, put it again in the box, and said to her : " Behold, you have well-nigh perished again through your curiosity."

He straightway left Psyche, and flew to Jupiter, the father of the gods, whom he entreated to intercede with Venus on Psyche's behalf. Accordingly Jupiter summoned all the gods to his presence, and commanded Mercury to bring Psyche into the palace of heaven. And then he took a vase filled with immortality, and said : " Psyche, drink that you may be immortal, and that Cupid may nevermore depart from you."

Immediately a great marriage feast was sumptuously prepared. The Hours decked the hall with roses, the Muses sang with celestial harmony, Apollo played upon the harp, and Venus danced to the music. Thus was Psyche married to Cupid, and became his everlasting wife.

Exercises.

I.

1. Why were the shrines of Venus deserted ?
2. Why was Psyche left alone in the mountains ?
3. How was she carried into the valley ?
4. How did Psyche learn who her husband was ?
5. Who was Psyche's husband ?

6. How did Cupid learn that Psyche had disobeyed
   his orders ?
7. What were Cupid's orders to his wife ?
8. What trials did Venus put upon Psyche ?
9. How did Psyche accomplish all the tasks which
   Venus ordered her to perform ?

II.

1. What is the meaning of the following words ?—
   sufficiently, neglected, warbling, fragrant,
   deprive, endeavour, snare, desolate, perish.
2. Find another word which can be put instead of
   the italicized words in
   (a) She was served at table by *unseen* hands.
   (b) He received in return this *dreadful* answer.
   (c) Why do you *marvel* at these riches ?
   (d) She *besought* the wind to carry her sisters
       into the valley.
   (e) They persuaded Psyche *to endeavour* to
       obtain sight of her husband.
   (f) A river flowed past her *dwelling*.

III.

Tell the following story, filling in the missing
parts in the way you consider best.
The linesman and his sons lived far from any other
    human beings. A great storm carried away
    the signal, and the swollen river broke down
    the bridge. In the afternoon the express
    would pass. The linesman and his sons
    planned to stop the train. . . . The express
    drew up within a few yards of the fatal spot.

The Pied Piper of Hamelin.

I.

Hamelin town 's in Brunswick,
  By famous Hanover city ;
The river Weser, deep and wide,
Washes its wall on the southern side ;
A pleasanter spot you never spied.
  But, when begins my ditty,
Almost five hundred years ago,
To see the townsfolk suffer so
From vermin, was a pity.

II.

Rats !
They fought the dogs, and killed the cats,
  And bit the babies in the cradles,
And ate the cheeses out of the vats,
  And licked the soup from the cooks' own ladles,
Split open the kegs of salted sprats,
Made nests inside men's Sunday hats,
And even spoiled the women's chats
  By drowning their speaking
  With shrieking and squeaking,
In fifty different sharps and flats.

III.

At last the people in a body
  To the Town Hall came flocking :
" 'Tis clear," cried they, " our Mayor 's a noddy ;

P

And as for our Corporation—shocking
To think we buy gowns lined with ermine
For dolts that can't or won't determine
What 's best to rid us of our vermin !
You hope, because you 're old and obese,
To find in the furry civic robe ease ?
Rouse up, sirs ! Give your brains a racking,
To find the remedy we 're lacking,
Or, sure as fate, we 'll send you packing ! "
   At this the Mayor and corporation
   Quaked with a mighty consternation.

IV.

An hour they sat in council ;
   At length the Mayor broke silence :
" For a guilder I 'd my ermine gown sell !
   I wish I were a mile hence !
It 's easy to bid one rack one's brain—
I 'm sure my poor head aches again,
I 've scratched it so, and all in vain.
Oh, for a trap, a trap, a trap ! "
Just as he said this, what should hap
At the chamber door but a gentle tap ?
" Bless us ! " cried the Mayor ; " what 's that ? "
(With the Corporation as he sat
Looking little, though wondrous fat ;
Nor brighter was his eye, nor moister
Than a too-long-opened oyster,
Save when at noon his paunch grew mutinous
For a plate of turtle green and glutinous),

" Only a scraping of shoes on that mat?
Anything like the sound of a rat
Makes my heart go pit-a-pat ! "

V.

" Come in ! " the Mayor cried, looking bigger :
And in did come the strangest figure !
His queer long coat from heel to head
Was half of yellow and half of red ;
And he himself was tall and thin,
With sharp blue eyes, each like a pin,
And light loose hair, yet swarthy skin,
No tuft on cheek nor beard on chin,
But lips where smiles went out and in ;
There was no guessing his kith and kin :
And nobody could enough admire
The tall man and his quaint attire.
Quoth one :   " It 's as my great-grandsire,
Starting up at the Trump of Doom's tone,
Had walked this way from his painted tombstone ! "

VI.

He advanced to the council-table :
And " Please your honours," he said, " I 'm able,
   By means of a secret charm, to draw
      creatures living beneath the sun,
That creep, or swim, or fly, or run,
   After me so as you never saw !
And I chiefly use my charm
On creatures that do people harm,

The mole and toad and newt and viper:
And people call me the Pied Piper."
(And here they noticed round his neck
A scarf of red and yellow stripe,
To match his coat of the self-same check:
And at the scarf's end hung a pipe:
And his fingers, they noticed, were ever straying
As if impatient to be playing
Upon this pipe, as low it dangled
Over his vesture so old-fangled.)
"Yet," said he, "poor piper as I am,
In Tartary I freed the Cham,
    Last June, from his huge swarm of gnats:
I eased in Asia the Nizam
    Of a monstrous brood of vampire bats:
And as for what your brain bewilders,
    If I can rid your town of rats,
Will you give me a thousand guilders?"
"One? Fifty thousand!" was the exclamation
Of the astonished Mayor and Corporation.

VII.

Into the street the Piper stept,
    Smiling first a little smile,
As if he knew what magic slept
    In his quiet pipe the while:
Then, like a musical adept,
To blow his pipe his lips he wrinkled,
And green and blue his sharp eyes twinkled,

Like a candle-flame where salt is sprinkled :
And ere three shrill notes the pipe uttered,
You heard as if an army muttered ;
And the muttering grew to a grumbling,
And the grumbling grew to a mighty rumbling ;
And out of the houses the rats came tumbling.
Great rats, small rats, lean rats, brawny rats,
Brown rats, black rats, grey rats, tawny rats,
Grave old plodders, gay young friskers,
    Fathers, mothers, uncles, cousins,
Cocking tails and pricking whiskers,
    Families by tens and dozens.
Brothers, sisters, husbands, wives,
Followed the Piper for their lives.
From street to street he piped advancing,
And step for step they followed dancing,
Until they came to the River Weser,
    Wherein all plunged and perished !
Save one, who, stout as Julius Cæsar,
Swam across, and lived to carry
    (As he, the manuscript he cherished)
To Rat-land home his commentary :
Which was : " At the first shrill note of the pipe,
I heard a sound as of scraping tripe,
And putting apples, wondrous ripe,
Into a cider-press's gripe :
And a moving away of pickle-tub-boards,
And a leaving ajar of conserve cupboards,
And a drawing the corks of train-oil flasks,
And a breaking the hoops of butter-casks :

And it seemed as if a voice
  (Sweeter far than by harp or by psaltery
Is breathed) called out, " O rats, rejoice !
  The world is grown to one vast drysaltery !
So munch on, crunch on, take your nuncheon,
Breakfast, supper, dinner, luncheon ! "
And just as a bulky sugar-puncheon,
All ready staved, like a great sun shone
Glorious, scarce an inch before me,
Just as methought it said, ' Come, bore me ! '
—I found the Weser rolling o'er me."

VIII.

You should have heard the Hamelin people
Ringing the bells till they rocked the steeple.
" Go," cried the Mayor, " and get long poles ;
Poke out the nests, and block up the holes !
  Consult with carpenters and builders,
And leave in our town not even a trace
Of the rats ! "—when suddenly, up the face
Of the Piper perked in the market-place,
  With a "First, if you please, my thousand guilders !"

IX.

A thousand guilders ! The Mayor looked blue ;
So did the Corporation too.
For Council dinners made rare havoc
With Claret, Moselle, Vin-de-grave, Hock ;
And half the money would replenish
Their cellar's biggest butt with Rhenish.

To pay this sum to a wandering fellow,
With a gipsy coat of red and yellow!
" Beside," quoth the Mayor, with a knowing wink,
" Our business was done at the river's brink;
We saw with our eyes the vermin sink,
And what's dead can't come to life, I think.
So, friend, we 're not the folk to shrink
From the duty of giving you something for drink,
And a matter of money to put in your poke;
But, as for the guilders, what we spoke
Of them, as you very well know, was in joke.
Besides, our losses have made us thrifty.
A thousand guilders! Come, take fifty!"

X.

The Piper's face fell, and he cried,
" No trifling! I can't wait. Beside,
I 've promised to visit by dinner-time
Bagdad, and accept the prime
Of the head-cook's pottage, all he's rich in,
For having left in the Caliph's kitchen
Of a nest of scorpions no survivor :
With him I proved no bargain-driver,
With you don't think I 'll bate a stiver!
And folks who put me in a passion
May find me pipe to another fashion."

XI.

" How!" cried the Mayor, " d 'ye think I 'd brook
Being worse treated than a cook?

Insulted by a lazy ribald,
With idle pipe and vesture piebald!
You threaten us, fellow? Do your worst,
Blow your pipe there till you burst!"

XII.

Once more he stept into the street,
And to his lips again
Laid his long pipe of smooth straight cane;
And ere he blew three notes (such sweet
Soft notes as yet musician's cunning
Never gave the enraptured air),
There was a rustling that seemed like a bustling
Of merry crowds justling at pitching and hustling;
Small feet were pattering, wooden shoes clattering,
Little hands clapping, and little tongues chattering;
And, like fowls in a farm-yard where barley is
    scattering,
Out came the children running.
All the little boys and girls,
With rosy cheeks, and flaxen curls,
And sparkling eyes, and teeth like pearls,
Tripping and skipping, ran merrily after
The wonderful music with shouting and laughter.

XIII.

The Mayor was dumb, and the Council stood
As if they were changed into blocks of wood,

Unable to move a step, or cry
To the children merrily skipping by;
And could only follow with the eye
That joyous crowd at the Piper's back.
But now the Mayor was on the rack,
And the wretched Council's bosoms beat,
As the Piper turned from the High Street
To where the Weser rolled its waters
Right in the way of their sons and daughters!
However, he turned from south to west,
And to Koppelberg Hill his steps addressed,
And after him the children pressed;
Great was the joy in every breast.
"He never can cross that mighty top!
He's forced to let the piping drop,
And we shall see our children stop!"
When, lo! as they reached the mountain-side
A wondrous portal opened wide,
As if a cavern was suddenly hollowed;
And the Piper advanced and the children followed;
And when all were in, to the very last,
The door in the mountain-side shut fast.
Did I say all? No! one was lame,
And could not dance the whole of the way;
And in after years, if you would blame
His sadness, he was used to say:
"It's dull in our town since my playmates left!
I can't forget that I'm bereft
Of all the pleasant sights they see,
Which the Piper also promised me.

"And after him the children pressed" (page 249)

For he led us, he said, to a joyous land,
Joining the town, and just at hand,
Where waters gushed and fruit-trees grew,
And flowers put forth a fairer hue,
And everything was strange and new ;
The sparrows were brighter than peacocks here,
And their dogs outran our fallow-deer ;
And honey-bees had lost their stings,
And horses were born with eagles' wings :
And just as I became assured
My lame foot would be speedily cured,
The music stopped, and I stood still,
And found myself outside the hill,
Left alone against my will,
To go now limping as before,
And never hear of that country more ! "

XIV.

Alas ! alas for Hamelin !
There came into many a burgher's pate
A text which says that heaven's gate
Opes to the rich at as easy a rate
As the needle's eye takes a camel in !
The Mayor sent east, west, north and south,
To offer the Piper, by word of mouth,
Wherever it was man's lot to find him,
Silver and gold to his heart's content,
If he 'd only return the way he went,
And bring the children behind him.

But when they saw 'twas a lost endeavour,
And Piper and dancers were gone for ever,
They made a decree that lawyers never
Should think their records dated duly
If, after the day of the month and year,
These words did not as well appear :
" And so long after what happened here
On the Twenty-second of July,
Thirteen hundred and seventy-six : "
And the better in memory to fix
The place of the children's last retreat,
They called it the Pied Piper's Street.
Where any one playing on pipe or tabor
Was sure for the future to lose his labour.
Nor suffered they hostelry or tavern
To shock with mirth a street so solemn ;
But opposite the place of the cavern
They wrote the story on a column,
And on the great church window painted
The same, to make the world acquainted
How their children were stolen away,
And there it stands to this very day.
And I must not omit to say
That in Transylvania there 's a tribe
Of alien people who ascribe
The outlandish ways and dress
On which their neighbours lay such stress,
To their fathers and mothers having risen
Out of some subterraneous prison,

Into which they were trepanned
Long ago, in a mighty band,
Out of Hamelin town in Brunswick land,
But how, or why, they don't understand.

R. Browning.

Exercises.

1. Where is Hamelin ?
2. What was the plague from which the towns-folk suffered ?
3. What was the payment that the Piper asked for his services ?
4. How did the Piper rid the town of rats ?
5. Why was the Piper angry with the Mayor ?
6. What was the punishment which the Piper in-flicted on Hamelin ?
7. Where did the children go when they followed the Piper ?
8. How did the Piper persuade the rats and the children to follow him ?
9. Describe the Piper's appearance and clothes.
10. Where did the Piper say he had been before coming to Hamelin ?

II.

1. Put the words in the following sentences in the order in which they would usually be :—
   (a) For a guilder I 'd my ermine gown sell.
   (b) At the scarf's end hung a pipe.
   (c) Into the street the Piper stept.
   (d) To blow his pipe his lips he wrinkled.
   (e) Once more he stept into the street,

> And to his lips again
> Laid his long pipe.

(f) Out came the children running.

2. **Find rhymes for :** mayor, squeaking, furry, gown, yellow, beard, walked, guessing, people, fifty, daughter, sadness.

III.

1. **Tell this story in your own words.**

2. **Give the Piper's account of what he did at Hamelin.**

3. **Long ago in the market-place in Rome there stood a statue of a man with his right arm upraised, and on the pedestal was written "Strike here." No one could explain the meaning of these words. One day, however, a poor student marked the spot where the shadow of the arm fell at noon, and, returning at night, removed the paving-stones and dug down. He soon came to a slab in which was fixed an iron ring. Raising the slab, he uncovered a flight of stone steps leading downwards.**

Finish this story.

Words.

I.

Words are among the most wonderful and most useful things that men and women have made. Each of us has a name, which is a word fastened or attached to him as a label, and without which we should find ourselves in continual difficulty. It would be equally awkward if any of the necessary words of our language was missing.

Although animals and birds make sounds, and can to a very small extent speak to one another, in comparison with human beings they can scarcely be said to talk. Hence man has been called the talking animal, and it is because he is able to speak that he is so superior to all other creatures that live upon the earth.

Language is very old; nobody knows how old. It has been calculated that men have existed as long as five hundred thousand years, if not longer : if that is so, the oldest words may have been made as far back as that time, which is so distant that it is impossible for us to imagine its remoteness.

Ages passed before men began to write these words. But written language is very ancient too. On the other hand, printing is an invention which is quite modern. Printing was first used in this country not much more than four hundred years ago.

Speaking is a very difficult thing to learn; for,

although boys and girls learn to speak while they are still quite small, and, when they come to school, can speak well and speak fast, it took all of them two or three years to find out how to do so. When we consider how many movements of the mouth, lips, tongue and throat have to be made in uttering even a simple sentence, we realize how marvellous it is that we should be able to speak quickly.

A word is a sound which has a distinct meaning. We use words for two very different purposes ; which are, to talk and to think. We use them to make other people understand what we are thinking about, and we also use them to help ourselves to form ideas. In the latter case, however, we do not usually utter them aloud. If we knew no words, we could not think properly.

Every word, however old, must have been made by some person, who was afterwards copied by other people until the word so made became the property of many. When a word becomes common it may fall out of use again, or it may last for a long time. Some words have a long life, but in the end even they die, and are utterly lost and forgotten.

Words have been made in various ways. The simplest method is an attempt to imitate a sound. A cuckoo is so called because of the sound which that bird utters : the word *bang* is as good an imitation of the sound of an explosion as the human mouth can frame : and *splash* is a copy of the noise caused by an object falling into water.

Another way is to take two old words and join them together. The word *steamship*, which means a particular kind of ship, is constructed, as can be seen, by combining the words *steam* and *ship*. Other words of this kind, which are continually being made, are *bookcase*, *waterfall*, *iceberg,* and *Englishman.*

Still another device is to take an old word and alter it by changing part of it, by adding a syllable at the beginning, or by adding a syllable at the end. *Gild* is made from *gold* by changing the vowel-sound. From *true* we have made *truth, untruth, truly, untruly, untrue, truthful, untruthful, truthfully, untruthfully, truthfulness,* and *untruthfulness.*

These are the most usual and most important ways of making words. There are five or six other ways, which are rarer, and some of which are very remarkable. Some words, like *jump*, *hurry*, and *boy* are unexplained. Others are made by shortening ; thus *nestle* was made by cutting the ending from *nestling*, which means a young bird. The word *gas* was manufactured by adding together g, a and s.

That all words are not equally old can be seen by examining many of them. In the sentence " She left the typewriter and went to the telephone," the words *typewriter* and *telephone*, which are the names of modern inventions, are no older than the things they represent. *She* is probably about six hundred years old, and the others are so ancient that it is quite unknown when they were first made.

Englishmen did not make all their words for themselves. Frequently, when in want of a new word,
they borrowed from some foreign language. As
a result, nearly every sentence that any one utters
contains words that have come to us from foreign
lands. It is natural that, when we speak of an animal,
or plant, or other thing which is found in other parts
of the world, but not in England, we should give to
it its foreign name, if we know what the name is.
Kangaroo is the name that the Australian black
men gave to that animal, and we borrowed the name
when we first learnt of the existence of the animal.
Tea and *silk* were originally Chinese words, and
came to us with the articles for which they stand
as names. *Cocoa* is a Mexican word, and *tomahawk*
was introduced into English from the speech of the
North American Indians.

The chief languages from which words have been
borrowed are Latin, French and Greek. There are
many hundreds of such words in English. *Angel*,
church, *dish* and *arithmetic* come from Greek ;
poison and *battle* from French ; and *wall*, *table*
and *animal* from Latin. *Table*, however, although
it was originally Latin, was borrowed from Latin
by French, and passed thence into English.

As everybody knows, all men do not speak the
same tongue. Many different languages are used
in different parts of the world. This is in some ways
unfortunate, because it prevents different nations
from understanding one another properly. Some-

time in the future, perhaps, all men will speak one universal tongue, If they do, it is possible that the world language will be English. Even now, no other tongue is as widespread as English : it is spoken in Australia, Canada, South Africa, and the United States, as well as in Great Britain and Ireland. It is the native speech of about one person in eight, if we count all the inhabitants of the globe. Therefore we should be careful to speak the best English that we can. The best English is called Standard English.

II.

To read is to turn printed or written words into spoken words. That, at least, is what happens when one reads aloud. It is also what happens when anyone reads silently, except that in this case the reader thinks the words instead of uttering them with his lips, mouth, and tongue. But reading is more than this : to be able to read means that one is able to understand the meaning of the printed or written words.

In reading aloud certain points are worth remembering. If possible, Standard English should be used ; that is to say, the reader should be careful to pronounce the words properly. He should also speak clearly. Thirdly, if he wants to read well, he should read as he would speak, for the natural expression, or manner, is the best. Fourthly, the

Q

places where the voice should pause for breath need attention. Each set of words is called a phrase, and a great deal of practice is needed before a reader can know where it is best to pause. It might be thought that the punctuation would show where the pauses ought to come ; but, though that is partly true, it is not altogether true.

III.

Every extract in this book, and every chapter of every book, consists of sentences. Every sentence can be broken up into words. A sentence, being the expression of a thought, is a group of words which together make sense. By themselves words do not make complete sense.

To make good sense a sentence must do two things. It must tell us what thing it is about, and it must tell us what is said about that thing. Of these two, the first is called the Subject of the sentence, and the second is called the Predicate. Every sentence consists of Subject and Predicate. For instance, in the sentence " The stars glitter in the frosty sky," the chief thing mentioned is " the stars," while the information given is that they glitter in the frosty sky ; that is to say, " The stars " is the Subject of the sentence, while " glitter in the frosty sky " is the Predicate. If you examine the following table you will see how sentences can be divided in this manner :—

Subject.	Predicate.
The giant	came towards the palace.
He	soon found his brothers.
The Piper	stept into the street.
Hard words	break no bones.
Who	was that ?
To eat and drink	are necessary for life.

The subject need not come first. In the sentence "At the door stood a little boy," "a little boy" is the Subject, and "stood at the door" is the Predicate.

The words which compose sentences can be arranged in kinds according to the work they do. There are eight such kinds, which are called the "Parts of Speech," and which are named Noun, Pronoun, Adjective, Verb, Adverb, Preposition, Conjunction and Interjection.

A word which is used as the name of something is called a Noun. In the sentence "An old magpie flew out of the tree," "magpie" is a noun.

When a word is used to describe something, it is called an Adjective. In the sentence "The day is fine," "fine" is an adjective, because it describes *day*, and in the previous sentence "old" is an adjective because it describes *magpie*.

Words which say something about a person or thing are called Verbs. In the first sentence "flew" is a verb. It used to be said that in every sentence there is a verb, and that it is not possible to make a predicate without using one. This, however, is not quite true. We can say "Every man for himself," where *every man* is the subject and *for himself* is the predicate, and neither of these contains a verb. Nevertheless, nearly every sentence contains a verb.

The other parts of speech are more difficult to understand. Pronouns are words used as substitutes for nouns. In "The peasant went home, because he had obtained a magic sack," *he* is used to avoid repeating the words *the peasant*, and is a pronoun.

Adverbs are words used to alter or extend the meaning of verbs, adjectives, or other adverbs, as in "The sun was shining *brightly*," where *brightly* tells us how the sun was shining.

Prepositions join nouns together, or verbs to nouns, and show the relation between them. In "Stand on the floor," *stand* and *floor* are joined by *on*, and in "There are many good fish in the sea," *fish* and *sea* are joined by *in*, which is a preposition.

Conjunctions join words or sentences together. *And* is the commonest conjunction.

Interjections are exclamations. "Oh!" and "Eh!" are interjections.

Of course, the same word can be used in several ways. In "The *race* is not always won by the swiftest runner," *race* is a noun, but in "You should have seen the boys *race* towards the river" it is a verb.

The study of words in this manner is called grammar.

IV.

Some words are sounded alike and spelt alike but have different meanings, others are sounded alike but spelt differently and have different meanings. A third sort consists of words which are spelt and pronounced differently but have the same meanings. Here are three lists of some words of these kinds :—

A.—Some words which are sounded and spelt alike but have different meanings.

bark (1) the outer covering of a tree.
(2) the cry of a dog.

bound (1) to leap up.
(2) the limit of a piece of ground.

cricket (1) a game.
(2) an insect.

fast (1) rapid.
(2) to go without food.

hide (1) the thick skin of certain animals.
(2) to conceal.

lean (1) thin.
(2) to hang sideways.

main (1) chief or principal.
(2) the sea.

mean (1) to have in mind.
(2) poor and inferior.

mint (1) a scented herb.
(2) a place where money is made.

page (1) one side of a leaf of a book.
(2) a boy employed as a servant.

rock (1) a large piece of stone.
(2) to move backwards and forwards.

stern (1) severe and grim.
(2) the hind part of a ship.

tender (1) a carriage attached to a railway engine.
(2) requiring careful handling.

B.—*Some different words which have the same meanings :—*

abode, dwelling.
almost, nearly.
begin, commence.
better, superior.
blunt, dull.
broad, wide.
change, alter.
clothes, dress.
disorder, confusion.
edge, border.
end, termination.
enlarge, magnify.
extraordinary, unusual.
face, countenance.
grow, increase.

kind, sort.
large, big, vast, huge, great, immense, enormous.
lessen, diminish.
level, flat.
like, similar.
marvellous, wonderful.
might, strength.
missing, lost.
result, consequence.
serious, solemn.
sharp, keen.
situation, position.
stay, remain.
strong, powerful.

hide, conceal.
join, combine.

unfasten, detach.
whole, entire, complete.

C.—*Some words which are pronounced alike but spelt differently:*

aloud, allowed.
ascent, assent.
ate, eight.
beach, beech.
bean, been.
bear, bare.
blew, blue.
bow, bough.
bury, berry.
cellar, seller.
choir, quire.
climb, clime.
council, counsel.
course, coarse.
deer, dear.
fate, fête.
fisher, fissure.
flower, flour.
great, grate.
hale, hail.
haul, hall.
hear, here.
heir, air.
him, hymn.

night, knight.
one, won.
pale, pail.
pare, pair, pear.
peace, piece.
practise, practice.
prey, pray.
principal, principle.
profit, prophet.
rain, reign.
read, red.
read, reed.
route, root.
sailor, sailer.
sale, sail.
seam, seem.
seen, scene.
sent, scent.
stare, stair.
stationary, stationery.
steel, steal.
stile, style.
tail, tale.
there, their.

horse, hoarse.

hour, our.

idol, idle.

lessen, lesson.

manner, manor.

weak, week.

wear, ware.

wood, would.

write, right.

D.—*150 common words which are difficult to spell:—*

1	actually	grammar	rescue
	addition	grey	sandwich
	alphabet	guest	Saturday
	always	guide	sauce
5	anchor	halfpenny	sausage
	ancient	heart	scheme
	animal	height	scissors
	answer	imagine	secret
	anxious	increase	seized
10	appearance	innocent	sensible
	autumn	island	sentence
	awkward	jealous	separate
	beautiful	labour	serpent
	believe	laughter	severe
15	bicycle	leisure	shadow
	British	library	shoulder
	business	lightning	similar
	cabbage	literary	singe
	carriage	magazine	soldier
20	chimney	manage	solemn
	colonel	meagre	sovereign

colour	medicine	special
column	merely	speech
coming	minute	subtract
25 conscious	monarch	succeed
crystal	money	summer
cupboard	muscle	surprise
curious	mystery	sword
definite	naughty	through
30 describe	necessary	thumb
different	neighbour	tongue
disappear	obey	travel
disguise	orange	variety
distant	passenger	vegetable
35 doubtful	people	visible
easily	picture	visitor
eighth	plague	weather
enemies	pleasure	Wednesday
enough	possess	welcome
40 excite	potato	wherever
expense	precede	whether
favourite	pretty	whisper
feeble	previous	whistling
fiery	proceed	wholly
45 flower	pronunciation	wicked
foreign	proper	wondrous
fulfil	prophet	wrapped
gardener	pursue	wrath
gauze	quay	wretched
50 giant	receive	wrist

Exercises.

1. **What words have the following meanings ?—**
   [There are several answers to each question.]

   (1) piercing in sound.   Answer : shrill.
   (2) a loud cry.
   (3) a number of sharp sounds quickly following
       each other.
   (4) a sudden sharp noise.
   (5) the shrill cry of an animal in pain.
   (6) a deep heavy sound.

2. **What is the meaning of each of the following**
   compound words ?—

   [Examples : a *bookcase* is a case for books ; a
   steamship is a ship driven by steam.]

   blackberry, footstep, cricket-bat, crestfallen, pay-
   day, fir-cone, cogwheel, bootlace, stowaway,
   key-ring, offshoot, walking-stick.

3. **What compound words mean the same as the**
   following phrases ?—

   (a) a book small enough to hold in the hand :
       an engine for putting out fire : a frog which
       lives in trees : a jug for holding water : a
       wheel which is driven by water.
   (b) proud of being rich ; not able to speak ; a
       ship used in fighting ; without shoes ; a man
       able to earn his living in many ways.

4. **Add to each of the following words an ending taken**
   from this list, and then use the words you have
   made in a sentence :—

   [Example :—*move*. Answer : *moveable*. All the
   moveable furniture was piled in one room.]

-*able*, -*er*, -*al*, -*ness*, -*th*, -*ful*, -*ment*,—*or*:
bright, sail, steal, laugh, music, power, wide, ex-
cite, bitter, grow, harm, drive, care, agree, refuse.

5 (a) Place a suitable syllable taken from the following list before these words :—
[Example : *head*, *behead*.]
a-, *be*-, *mis*-, *un*-, *for*-, *en*-, *dis*-, *non*-, *de*-,
deed, wise, get, sense, come, circle, tangle, sleep,
cover, camp, bid, take, fire, bold, twist, side.
(b) Use each of the new words in a sentence.

6. (a) Make as many words as you can with the
italicized part of the following, in the manner
shown in the example :—
[Example—com*pose*, re*pose*, ex*pose*, de*pose*,
pro*pose*.]
sub*tract*, re*ception*, *cap*tain, *friend*ly,
ef*fect*, con*tain*, *honour*, *ease*.

(b) State the meaning of each of the words you
have made, using a dictionary to help you,
if necessary.

7. Mark the accented syllable in the following words :
[Example :—children. *Answer* : chíldren.]
hearty, unfold, crossing, reading, alone, always,
refuge, understand, dreamily, despair, compare,
upset, decide, decision, portion, composition,
destroy, destiny, difference, railway, separate,
station, footsore, yesterday, Monday, brother,
hero, warlike, artist, open, womanly, enjoyment,
London, Liverpool, Aberdeen.

8. Find words which mean the same as :—
journey, ship, difficult, finish, leap, evil, attack,

fear, amazement, hit, fancy, eat, cease, enough, food, angry, scent, sign.

9. Find words which mean the opposite of :—
    [Example :—right, wrong.]
crooked, black, skilful, close, solid, alive, hard, cold, true, ugly, fresh, fear, hate, rude, dry, rough.

10. Divide the following sentences into subject and predicate (see p. 261).

(a) Tom Brown sat in the big dining room. The table was covered with a white cloth. The stout head waiter brought in a tray. The tea and toast and poached eggs were hot. This is a famous breakfast. Tom ate a big breakfast. He paid the head waiter out of his own pocket.

Bright shines the sun. On this frosty morning, a coach is a cold place. The coachman asked Tom the following question :—" Are you going to school ? " Tom said " Yes." After all, it was a glorious ride. In a few minutes they had reached the town. Up the long street rattled the coach.

(b) The space under the window was occupied by a square table.

(c) Now the last minutes of the dance have come.

(d) On they rush across the playground.

11. In the following sentences state whether each italicized word is a noun, adjective, or verb, and in every case add the reason :—

THE STORM.

There had been a *wind* all day, and it was rising, with a *loud sound*. In another *hour* it *increased* greatly. *Sharp gusts* of *rain came* up before the *storm*, like *showers* of *steel*. When the *day broke* it *blew* harder and harder. *Great trees* were torn out of the *earth*.

All the while the *coach* was approaching the *coast*. Long before we *saw* the *sea*, its *spray* was on our *lips*, and *showered salt rain* upon us. The *water* was out over *miles* and miles of the *flat country* near to *Yarmouth*, and *every little puddle lashed* its *banks*. When we *reached* the *town* and *came* within *sight* of the *sea*, the *waves* on the *horizon* were so *huge* that they *looked* like another *shore* with *towers* and *buildings*. The *streets* of Yarmouth were strewn with *sand* and *seaweed* and *broken slates* blown from the *roofs* of *houses*. Half the *people* were out of *doors* watching the sea, and lurking behind buildings to *avoid* the *fierce fury* of the *gale*.

PRINTED IN GREAT BRITAIN BY
DAVID J. CLARK LIMITED, 34-38 CADOGAN STREET, GLASGOW, C.9

a